REALES ALCAZARES
de Sevilla

Text

Javier Lobato Domínguez
Angel Martín Esteban

Photographs by Miguel Angel Nistal and
EDITORIAL ESCUDO DE ORO, S.A.

Diagrams and reproduction
entirely conceived and produced by
EDITORIAL ESCUDO DE ORO, S.A.

Editorial Escudo de Oro, S.A.

Façade of the Palace of Rey Don Pedro. Lithography after a drawing by Girault de Prangey (1837).

INTRODUCTION

The Reales Alcázares of Seville form a monumental site of extraordinary density and complexity in terms of chronology, spaces and function. For this is not just one palace, but many palaces, adjoining and superimposed one on another. Here we find, side by side, a military stronghold with walls surrounding fine courtyards, the drifting scents of gardens and the murmuring of fountains and, over and above all, the permanent stature of the site as a repository of power. All this, under the ever-changing light of the Sevillian sky, full of different hues. The architecture takes those who enter its walls or contemplate it, back to a world where the fundamental concern of master builders, gardeners, musicians and poets was to create a place for the exaltation of the senses. Each shadow, each breeze softly flitting along galleries and corridors was studied and measured over ten centuries during which each wall has been restored a hundred times to remain always in the same place. Permanence, fragility, change and continuity co-exist in this unique palace, the seat of Moorish dignitaries and princes during the Islamic reign over a city which was then known as Isbiliya (10th-13th centuries) and later, from 1248 to the present day, the Sevillian residence of the Spanish monarchs.

For the art historian and the archaeologist, the building is a veritable jigsaw puzzle in which, as in a palimpsest written and erased many times, each space has been rebuilt and restored, the work sometimes transforming its appearance and at others merely altering some minor element. The multiplicity of the palace is reflected in the words of the poet Juan de Mal-Lara on the occasion of the visit of Philip II to the Reales Alcázares in 1570: «The Alcázar is a site of great space and freshness, and the Monarchs will not disdain to live here, for, though this is an ancient work, and many parts have been changed and made more modern, the entrances and the layout of the dependencies were always left as they were». The palace interposes remains of Caliphal and Taifan architecture (walls, doorways, capitals, columns and fountains) in the new Islamic forms of the Almohade empire, whose main court in the Al-Andalus region was precisely the Alcázar. All this is almost completely hidden below the Mudéjar splendour of the Palace of King Pedro (14th century) which respected the former Gothic palace of Alphonse X (13th) and forms the bases of the Reales Alcázares. Large-scale extensions and reforms were carried out in the 15th, 16th and 17th centuries, slowly transforming the building into a maze of rooms, courtyards, galleries and gardens. The plans and information provided in this guide are designed to form a thread to guide intrepid explorers in the adventure of visiting this ancient labyrinth.

We shall now give a brief description of the main historic events which have marked the life of this palace, compressing its over one thousand years of life into a short summary. The site now occupied by the Reales Alcázares of Seville were once open fields outside the walls of Roman Hispalis, crossed by a path which led from the nearby city gate to the Forum of the Corporations, or commercial centre of the city in the times of the Roman Empire. Here, and on the sandy stretches of land near the river was where the intensive activities of the port took place. A little further off, by the sides of the path and occupying what is now San Telmo, the tobacco factory, and part of the Huerta de la Alcoba, was the necropolis or City of the Dead. At some point, during the 3rd or 4th century, perhaps, a temple to Isis was built on the site of what is now the Reales Alcázares, a sculpture of that god having been found in the Patio de la Montería in the Alcázar in 1606.

Reliable records begin to be available with the Christian era, when a Visigoth basilica was built on the site now occupied by the Patio de Banderas and the Apeadero de los Reales Alcázares. The basilica has been identified with that known by narrative sources as of San Vicente, and was where the remains of the Christian martyr Saint Vincent were kept. The fact that the basilica contained the burial-place of an important saint, besides being outside the city walls, leads us to think that it was cemeterial in type, similar to those in the great dioceses of North Africa (Carthage) or Rome. The interior and surrounding areas will have been occupied by hundreds of tombs of faithful who paid to be as close as possible to the relics of the martyr, in the belief that on Judgement Day he would intercede for them. Chronicles also indicate that Saint Isidro, Saint Leandro and Saint Honorato were buried here. In 1976, part of this early Christian church was excavated, with the result that the baptistry was unearthed.

After the Moorish conquest of Seville in the year 712, part of the basilica was used as a mosque until it was completely destroyed by the Normans in 844. The persistence of the monumental architecture, located on the same sites formerly occupied by great religious or defensive buildings, whether for motives of prestige or strategic position, explains why, very soon, the Moorish princes chose this place for the construction of a palace, initially with more the character of a fortress than a luxurious residence.

The years 844 and 913 are cited as those when new Alcázares were built in Isbiliya, as Seville was known to the Moors. There were, perhaps, two stages in the construction of the only site still standing, known as the Dar al Imara, or governor's palace, as it was the seat of the Ummal, or political chiefs who exercised power on behalf of the Cordoban emirs and caliphs. Its high walls, built of great hewn stones and de-

Almohade arches in the second house in the Patio de Banderas.

fended by square towers, can be seen from Plaza del Triunfo, Calle Joaquín Romero Murube, Plaza de la Alianza, Calle Rodrigo Cano and Calle Judería, as well as from inside the Reales Alcázares. The parade ground of this original palace was what is now the Patio de Banderas.

The 11th century saw the beginning of the process of extensions and additions to the principal nucleus of the palace, with each new dynasty building a residence adjoining the original buildings or rebuilding and enlargening the original structure. The first palace to be described in poems and chronicles as a superb mansion of singular beauty was that built by Al Mutadid ibn Abbad and his son Al Mutamid, kings of Seville from 1041 to 1091. This new residence, the Alcázar al Mubarak, or of the Blessing, was built adjoining the original Dar al Imara, but of its patios and rooms little now remains. The central patio of the domestic area was rebuilt during the Almohade period (12th-13th centuries) and was recently excavated and restored as the seat of the Department of Public Works, adjoining the Reales Alcázares on its western side. The most luxurious room in the Al Mubarak was the Al Turayya, or room of the Pleiads, covered by a huge dome and surrounded by another five rooms. Al Mutamid brought marble from the Medina Azahara, the gardened city of the Cordoban caliphs, to decorate this chamber, where his throne stood. The walls and arches of the structure of the Salón de Embajadores in the present Reales Alcázares are remains of the original Al Turayya, where the poet king composed some of his works, full of sensuality and which he bitterly recalls in other poems after his defeat and exile in Africa.

The Almohade empire chose Seville as its main capital in Al-Andalus, their caliphs residing here, promoting great urban reforms which transformed it into a monumental city. Besides the new mosque and its minaret, the Giralda, and pleasure palaces outside the city, such as La Buhaira, they also restored and extended the Alcázares, to which were added patios, rooms and fortified areas, converting the site into a veritable citadel occupying the entire southern angle of Seville. To this period date the Garden of El Crucero or of María de Padilla, the Stucco Palace and the reconstruction of the main patio of the Palace of Al Mutadid. The walls of the Alcázar of Abu Hafs, whose defensive towers were the Torre del Oro and the Torre de la Plata, still stand beside the river. Part of the walls of the gardens and some of the rooms and vaults of the palace date also date back to the Almohade period.

On 22 December 1248, Ferdinand III, King of Castile and Leon, sanctified in the 17th century, entered solemnly into the city of Seville after a two-year siege. Sayyid Saqqaf, Axatef in the Christian chronicles, had signed the capitulation obliging the Moors to surrender the city «libre e quita» and giving the population one month to leave the city. Legend attributes to the son of Saint Ferdinand, the future King Alphonse X, the fierce threat to the vanquished that, should they dare destroy any buildings in the city, particularly the mosque minaret: «if just one brick is removed, I will put all Moors to the sword». The Palatine site of the Alcázares therefore passed intact into the possession of the crown of Castile, which installed its court here. Ferdinand III died in the Reales Alcázares of Seville on 30 May 1252, succeeded by his son Alphonse X, the Wise (1252-1284). The new king ordered the construction of a palace inside the Alcázares. This, due to its four staircases, would become known as the Room of the Snail, or Gothic Palace. This work signified the Christianisation of a sector of the Palatine residence and followed the dictates of Gothic style as practised by the masters then working on the construction of Burgos Cathedral and the Monastery of Las Huelgas. There is no record of further building work here until the 14th century, when documents refer to reforms carried out under Alphonse XI (1312-1350) and, in particular, his son, Pedro I (1350-1369). The former ordered the construction of the Chamber of Justice adjoining the Patio del Yeso, the first dependency in Mudéjar style to be built within the Palatine site. Alphonse XI, a king who gave new impulse to the Christian reconquest, demonstrated his allegiance to the knightly ideals praised in epic stories and poems by founding the Knightly Order of the Band, whose emblem a shield crossed diagonally by a band emerging from two dragons, appears frequently in the decoration of the Reales Alcázares. It was, however, Pedro I, known in the chronicles as the Cruel or the Judge, who transformed a large area of the site by building his palace on remains from the 11th and 12th centuries. The Alcázar of Pedro I was the most important palatial civil building in Mudéjar style completed to date by the Castilian court. The work was carried out in part by Moorish craftsmen sent by the Nasrite king of Granada and by Mudéjar master builders from Toledo and Seville. The result is a palace of spectacular beauty which combines the delicacy of stucco work and lattice work similar to the Alhambra in Granada with the colourful brilliance of the covering of Sevillian tiles and the thematic and decorative variety of work in stone, wood and plaster of the Toledan craftsmen. Pedro I is one of the most attractive figures in the Spain of the Middle Ages. Trained in all the princely arts, Pedro was a firm believer in the divine right of kings and a great admirer of the knightly values of lineage, loyalty and strength. This placed him in conflict with the powerful Castilian nobility, and he therefore sought the support of the emerging urban bourgeoisie and of the cultural elites. The civil war he waged against his brother, Henry of Trastamara, took on international proportions with the intervention of armies from Aragon, Granada, France and England. Pedro was ruthless in punishing those he considered traitors and after his assassination at the hands of the pretender to the throne Henry II, his figure was besmirched with terrible tales, leading him to become known as «the Cruel».

After the death of Pedro I, the Castilian monarchs who followed after him transferred their court back to their palaces in Castile, where they spent large periods. The Reales Alcázares of Seville were then left to the care of their alcaides, or governors, remaining practically unchanged as the second residence of kings and queens, who made only brief visits here. The only work of note carried out before Isabel I ascended the throne was the construction of the coffered dome in the Salón de Embajadores during the reign of King John II (1427). This situation changed completely during the reign of the Catholic Monarchs (1476-1504), when Seville was seat of the court for long periods and the Alcázares were extended with new apartments, galleries and miradores (viewpoints), adorned with coffering, frescoes and figurative tiles. The palace was the scene of important festivities whenever the monarchs took up residence, or when Prince John, heir to the two crowns, was born within the walls of this historic site, but due to whose early death, the succession passed to Charles I. The discovery of America also left its mark on the Reales

View of the labyrinth in the Cenador de la Alcoba. ▷

Alcázares, as Queen Isabel dedicated part of the site as the Casa de Contratación, from where new expeditions were organised and were tax controls were exercised over trade with the New World.

The Modern Age began in Spain with a change in dynasty in the shape of the rise of the House of Austria to the throne in the person of Charles I (1517-1556), who was proclaimed emperor in 1519. The Reales Alcázares in the richest and most highly populated city in the kingdom, played an important role in the life of Charles I, as it was here that his wedding with Isabel of Portugal took place. The palace was richly decorated in preparation for this great event, and the revelry was continuous from the entry into the city of the future queen on 3 March 1526 until the couple left the city for Granada on 18 May. The emperor himself chose the palace as the setting for the wedding, which took place in the Salón de Embajadores, and the memory of those happy times lives on in the work carried out throughout the 16th century here. The rooms of the Gothic Palace have been known since then as the Salas de las Fiestas, whilst the gardens were embellished with the first maze, a grotto and a pleasure pavilion - the Cenador de la Alcoba - a miniature architectural masterpiece in the idyllic setting of the former orange grove of the Islamic Palace. Philip II (1556-1598), known as the «bureaucratic king», who from his office controlled the day-to-day running of an empire on which the sun never set, took similar care of the decoration and improvement of his palaces, gardens and hunting grounds, decreeing a programme of construction and regulation to be carried out by the Royal Junta of Works and Forests, a body set up in 1545 to oversee the royal estates. He made a brief visit to inspect his possessions in Seville in May 1570, but the palace improvements continued throughout his entire reign.

During the 17th century, the Reales Alcázares received the visit of the crown prince of England, who came to Spain incognito in 1623 to negotiate his marriage to the king's sister, and that of King Philip IV himself the following year. The Palace alcaide was then Gaspar de Guzmán, Count-Duke of Olivares and king's favourite, who ordered the royal apartments to be duly prepared, restoring the building and its gardens, which took on a more modern aspect due to the works carried out by the Italian maestro mayor, Vermondo Resta. The lavish banquets and feasts with which the prince was fêted during his stay were complemented by performances of plays, hunts and celebrations organised at the Royal Palace of El Lomo del Grullo, adjoining the Hermitage del Rocío. These festivities were further continued with the celebrated banquet offered by the Duke of Medina Sidonia at El Coto de Doñana.

The change of century also saw another change in the royal dynasty. Charles II, the «bewitched» king, died heirless, and the last monarch of the House of Austria was succeeded by his nephew, Philip of Bourbon, Philip V, though he had to fight for his throne against the Austrian pretender. The War of Spanish Succession, defeats in Europe and the legacy of decades of misgovernment left the country impoverished and without morale. The new king, despite certain attempts at reform, did not seem better able to rule the country than had his predecessors. The victim of frequent deep depressions which bordered on delirium, in 1729 the king came to Seville to rest and recover from his «melancholy». The court remained in the city for five years, years of continuous festivities to pay for which the local authorities exhausted the city treasury. The health of the king, cosseted by his second wife, the Italian Isabel of Farnesio, was not improved by the baroque performances staged at the Reales Alcázares - bullfights, firework displays, concerts, opera and plays - and he preferred to hunt in the grounds around Seville, to spend hours fishing in the large pond in the gardens or to sail on the Guadalquivir in the gilded, velvet-upholstered gondola given to him by the cabildo hispalense. During the hot summer months, he left the city on board this luxurious vessel to take up residence at El Puerto de Santa María.

In consequence of the five years the king was in residence here, the palace was greatly renovated, for rather than great new works, the original apartments were restored and rebuilt, with some zones being conserved which otherwise would have fallen into ruin. The palace saw the birth of the Infanta María Antonia Fernanda, and it was from here that Isabel's first-born, Charles, left to reign first in Tuscany and later in Naples. The prince did not return to Spain until 1759 to succeed his parents on the throne as Charles III.
The rest of the 18th century was a time of more misfortunes than benefits for the Royal Palace, the departure of the court and the earthquake of 1775 causing severe damage to befall both the building and the surrounding gardens. The marvellous Almohade Garden of El Crucero was ruined and its underground flowerbeds were filled in, whilst new arches and galleries were built at either end. Only the determination of such illustrious governors as Francisco de Bruna or Pablo de Olavide helped to maintain and renew cultural activity at the Reales Alcázares. Its rooms housed the newly-created Academies of the Three Noble Arts and of Letters, whilst Bruna lent these institutions works of art such as drawings by Murillo or paintings by Velazquez, as well as beginning a small museum with sculptures and other works brought from Italica. Years previously, Olavide had held discussions with some of the most influential writers of the moment, including Jovellanos, in his house in the Reales Alcázares. In 1796, the palace fleetingly recaptured its old brilliance and vitality with the visit of Charles IV, his family and a following of 1,541 people. Once more, the daily routine was broken up by the celebration of feasts, bullfights, luminarias and religious festivities.

The 19th century was tragically marked by the slow agony of the old regime and absolutist monarchy and the struggle to impose a bourgeois liberal regime. And the Alcázar of Seville continued to be a faithful witness to historic events. During the French occupation, the palace became once more became the seat of a new administration and residence of the usurper, King Joseph I during his brief stay in Seville. During this period, the government of occupation concealed an act of premeditated pillage beneath the mask of performing the enlightened task of opening a great museum devoted to the Sevillian pictoric school in the Reales Alcázares. Under this pretext, the rooms of the palace were filled with around one thousand paintings, among them masterpieces by Pacheco, Velazquez, Zurbarán and Murillo, brought here from churches, convents and the homes of private citizens. When Seville was abandoned by the retreating French troops, they took with them a selection of some 400 of these works.

The first half of the 19th century was, as we have said, a period of neglect and misgovernment of the palace, left in the hands of alcaides and administrators of scarce capacity and less vision. It was during this time that some of the most unfortunate interventions were made in the architecture and decoration of the Alcázares. The fine stucco work was crudely whitewashed over, many of the rooms were abandoned, furniture and paintings from them were lost, the upper gallery of the Patio de Doncellas was closed off by glazed partitions and its original decoration was destroyed.

After 1850, the first studies and guides to the Reales Alcázares began to be published, whilst the Romantic movement, with its passion for the Oriental and its appreciation of medieval architecture, helped the palace to become seen as a masterpiece of civil Mudéjar. Unfortunately, however, the criteria for the restoration of the building at that time emphasised the picturesque effect and the recreation of spaces to give them a supposedly historic ambience rather than the conservation and study of the original elements in order to extend comprehension of the different stages in the construction of the palace. The consequence was the indiscriminate reproduction of stucco work using moulds wherever these had been damaged or were required to give «atmosphere», some even being copies of works already existing in the Alhambra, at times installed upside-down. The decoration of the walls was cleared of the thick layer of whitewash with which it had been covered at the beginning of the century, but the ornamental motifs thus revealed once more were painted in bright colours bearing little

Pages 10-11: Aerial view of the Reales Alcázares. ▷

resemblance to the original design. The section which most suffered from the «restoration work» of 1855 was the upper area of the Patio de Muñecas, rebuilt according to the misguided criteria of Rafael Contreras. Two important events took place here during the closing decades of the last century: firstly, the improved training received by historians, architects and archaeologists allowed more scientific study of the site, leading to interventions which treated the building with more respect with the aim, not of inventing, but of preserving. An example of this new attitude was the discovery, study and controversial restoration of the Patio del Yeso. Secondly, the palace continued to fulfil the function of royal residence after the Bourbons had been restored once more in the person of King Alphonse XII. In 1878, the upper floor of the palace was converted into the residence of the Queen Mother Isabel II who, nevertheless, after a brief stay in Seville, manifested a preference for her Parisian palace over the Reales Alcázares. Due to this restoration work, however, most of the furniture, paintings and ornaments in the upper apartments date back to the late-19th century, leaving an important Isabelline mark on the royal residence.

During the first third of the 20th century, the Reales Alcázares maintained their double function as residence of King Alphonse XIII and Queen Victoria Eugenia when they were in the city, and an artistic monument receiving ever greater numbers of visits from tourists and art lovers. The king named the Marquis of Vega Inclán royal commissioner for tourism, and the palace and its urban surroundings were restored and improved under his personal supervision. Amongst the reforms carried out we can mention the acquisition of the entrance of the dukes of Arcos in Marchena for installation adjoining the Torre del Agua. The gardens were also greatly extended through the transformation of the old vegetable gardens of La Alcoba and El Retiro into parks, arbours and flowerbeds. Socles, stucco work and coffering were restored under the direction of palace architects José Gómez Otero (1874-1920) and his son, José Gómez Millán.

On the restoration of the Republic in 1931, the crown lands and possessions passed into the hands of the state. The Reales Alcázares were, however, transferred to the possession of Seville City Council by the republican government on 22 April 1931. Since then, the city authorities have been the proprietors of the palace site and gardens, designating their curators. In 1988, an agreement was signed between the Governing Board of the National Heritage Commission, the body responsible for running the royal palaces of Spain, and Seville City Council regulating the use of the new Royal Apartments in the Reales Alcázares by the King and Queen and members of the Royal Family, thus continuing a tradition which has lasted for over six centuries according to which this palace is the residence and court of the Spanish. monarchy. On 30 November 1992, the council founded the Royal Alcázar Trust, the institution which has since then managed and conserved the building.
We should not like to end this introduction without making a modest proposal to visitors to the Royal Palace. This proposal is none other than to allow themselves to trust their own sensitivity. The reader will find in the pages of this guide details, dates and names, information garnered from the vast bibliography on the theme of the palace and from documents from its own important archives, the property of the National Heritage Commission and which forms a veritable historical memory of the palace and its past inhabitants. But it can be no bad thing for visitors to the Reales Alcázares of Seville to leave this objective description to one side for a moment, setting our imaginations free as we wander, as did the Romantics of the last century, among whom Washington Irving was an outstanding figure. His Tales of the Alhambra (1832) might well have been stories about the Alcázar if the palace had not in those days had such a domestic air, so officiously inhabited by its alcaide and administrators. Now, travellers coming to the palace can not only take their guidance from the pages of this book, but may also give free rein to their steps and gaze, following the path their senses and their sensitivity lead them.

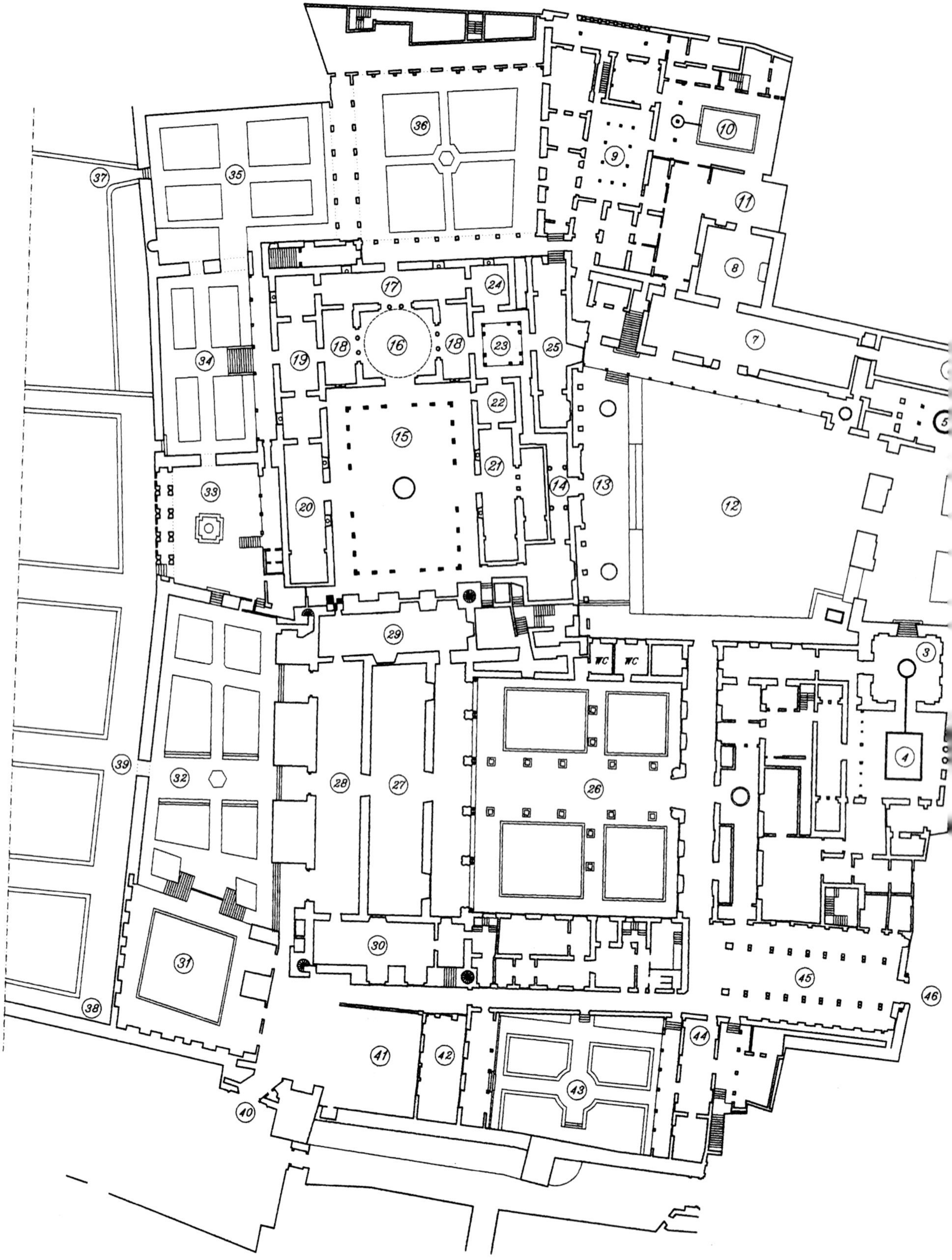

36
10
9
35
37
11
8
17
24
7
16
18
18
19
23
25
34
5
22
15
21
13
14
33
20
12
29
3
WC
WC
4
26
39
32
28
27
31
30
45
46
38
44
41
42
43
40

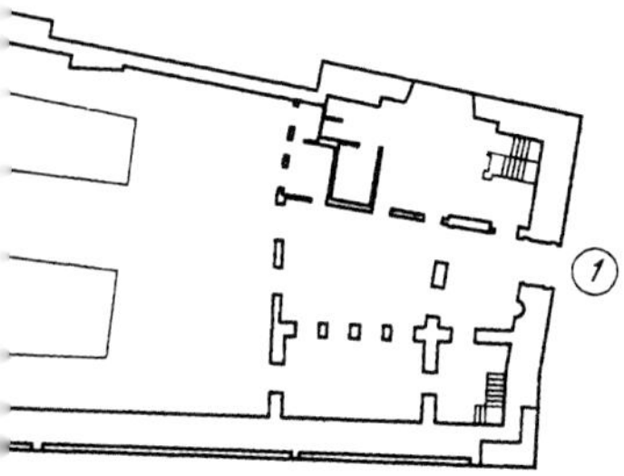

1. - PUERTA DEL LEON
2. - PATIO DEL LEON
3. - SALA DE LA JUSTICIA
4. - PATIO DEL YESO
5. - CUARTO MILITAR
6. - CASA DE LA CONTRATACION. SALA I
7. - SALA II O DEL ALMIRANTE
8. - SALA CAPITULAR O CAPILLA
9. - PATIO DEL ASISTENTE
10. - PATIO DE LEVIES
11. - PATIO DE ROMERO MURUBE
12. - PATIO DE LA MONTERIA
13. - FACHADA DEL PALACIO MUDEJAR
14. - VESTIBULO
15. - PATIO DE LAS DONCELLAS
16. - SALON DE EMBAJADORES
17. - SALA DEL TECHO DE FELIPE II
18. - SALAS COLATERALES AL SALON DE EMBAJADORES
19. - HABITACIONES DE INFANTES
20. - SALON DEL TECHO DE CARLOS V
21. - CAMARA Y ALCOBA REGIA
22. - SALA DE PASOS PERDIDOS
23. - PATIO DEL TECHO DE LAS MUÑECAS
24. - SALA DE LOS REYES CATOLICOS
25. - CUARTO DEL PRINCIPE
26. - PATIO DEL CRUCERO
27. - SALON DE TAPICES
28. - SALA DE AZULEJOS
29. - CAPILLA GOTICA
30. - SALA CANTARERA
31. - ESTANQUE DE MERCURIO
32. - JARDIN DE LA DANZA
33. - JARDIN DE TROYA
34. - JARDIN DE LA GALERA
35. - JARDIN DE LAS FLORES O DE LA GRUTA VIEJA
36. - JARDIN DEL PRINCIPE
37. - JARDIN DEL LABERINTO VIEJO O DE LA CRUZ
38. - GALERIA DE GRUTESCO
39. - JARDIN DE LAS DAMAS
40. - PUERTA DE MARCHENA
41. - JARDIN DEL CHORRON
42. - PABELLON DE LA CHINA
43. - JARDIN DE LA ALCUBILLA
44. - TIENDA DE RECUERDOS
45. - APEADERO
46. - PUERTA DEL PATIO DE BANDERAS

REALES ALCAZARES DE SEVILLA

PLANTA GENERAL

JESUS MARQUINEZ RENGIFO

Walls, and Calle Joaquín Romero Murube.

Walls and the Gate of the Patio de Banderas. ▷

II. GUIDE

WALLS AND DOORS

As a medieval construction, the Alcázares of Seville combined their residential function with an important military component, being simultaneously palace and fortress. The site is defended by high walls and towers, as well as taking advantage of such natural defences as the Guadalquivir River and the old Tagarete gully.

The first fortified area was the Dar al Imara, or Governor's Palace, built in the 9th century after the Norman attack on Seville in 844 and rebuilt during the reign of Abderramán III (913). This area is rectangular in shape, irregular particularly in the east side, with strong walls in which carved stone alternates with stretcher and header. These walls feature thick towers, barely salient, whose base presents a scarp in the form of a slight talus. The northern stretch of walls can be seen from Plaza del Triunfo and Calle Joaquín Romero Murube, the rest being hidden by constructions forming part of the Patio de Banderas and the Reales Alcázares. The visitor can observe six of the original towers on this side, as well as the keep, or Torre de Homenaje, built later (11th century). Calle Joaquín Romero Murube conserves the main gate to this first Alcázar, its noble Moorish arch now blind. Access to what used to be the parade ground of the Dar Al Imara, now Patio de Banderas, is through a wicket gate in the form of a semicircular arch over which is a ceramic panel bearing the royal coat of arms, a late-19th century work based on a design by José Gestoso. Above this tile is a defensive machicolation supported by two great brackets.

The Puerta del León, a gateway opened up in the Moorish walls during the 14th-century, was thereafter the main entrance to the buildings making up the Reales Alcázares. The gate, flanked by two towers, is situated in the angle formed by the Dar al Imara (9th-10th centuries) and the 11th-century Al Muwarak Abaddite Alcázar. The entrance is formed by a stilted semicircular arch adorned by a frieze in slight relief. Originally, this arch must have been Moorish, in the form of a horseshoe arch, its curve being «Christianised» by cutting off the lower voussoirs. The tiled panel crowning it gives the gate its name, as a framed section features a heraldic lion with royal crown, cross and spear bearing the legend Ad Utrumque. This figure represents the triumph of the Reign of the Lion over its enemies and the legitimacy of the royal dynasty, inherited from the Visigoth and Asturian kings symbolised by the cross of victory, emblem of the Kingdom of Asturias. The work, dating back to the year 1894, is by Fernando Soto Gónzalez after a design by José Gestoso, as is recorded in the inscription on the base: «Siendo Alcaide de estos Reales

REALES ALCAZARES

Puerta del León.

Alcázares el Excmo. Sr. Marqués de Irún, José Gestoso Fecit, 1894. Fabrica de Mensque Hno. y Cia. Triana». The work replaced an earlier painting by Joaquín Domínguez Bécquer in 1844. The whole is crowned by a machicolation supported by stone brackets.
The palace gardens are delimited by ruins of the old Taifan and Almohade walls of the Reales Alcázares and by the outer walls of the Jewish quarter.

PATIO DE LA MONTERIA - LEON

This patio, giving entrance to the Reales Alcázares, is made up of two spaces divided by an Almohade wall with three arches. The central of these, the largest, still conserves traces of heraldic decoration dating back to the 14th century in the form of castles and lions, whilst on the side panels between the arches are small blind interlinking Moorish arches. Both patios are traditionally known as the Patio de la Montería, possibly because this was where the royal huntsmen assembled for hunting expeditions. Since the last century, the first patio has been known as that of El León, however, due to the decoration of the gate giving access to the area. The combination of the different spaces and gates provide a fine setting to the contemplation of the main element, the façade of the Mudéjar Palace of Pedro I.
The Theatre or Corral of La Montería was built in the first patio during the 17th century (1625). This was the main centre of Sevillian theatre, the principal stage for performances of the comedies and dramatic works of

Almohade wall separating the Puerta del León from the Patio de la Montería.

the most outstanding playwrights of the Spanish Siglo de Oro. This work by palace maestro mayor Vermondo Resta, commissioned by Alcaide Gaspar de Guzmán, Count-Duke of Olivares. Its eliptically-shaped stage was surrounded by three tiers of seats. The theatre was the scene of many incidents and clashes between supporters and detractors of different authors and companies, forcing the intervention of the royal stewards and the imprisonment of more than one trouble-maker in the nearby palace gaol. It was destroyed by fire on 3 May 1691, the flames also damaging the adjoining Casa de la Contratación.

Chamber of Justice and Patio de Yeso

The Chamber of Justice was built during the reign of Alphonse XI and is the first example of Mudéjar art in

Patio del León.

Patio de la Montería.

the Alcázar, its decoration showing the influence of Toledan art. Like the Moorish Qubbas, the room is square, and is covered with ornately-decorated bevelled coffering with from whose central space must once have hung a mocarab pendant. Outstanding are the stucco decorations of the room, whilst in the upper third is a frieze with windows closed by lattices of different forms: *ataurique* (decorative stucco relief), geometric wheels, etc. In the middle are stuccoed blind arches, whilst the usual tiled base is not to be found as, in this case, the more economic solution of painting it was adopted. The room is oriented towards the Patio del Yeso, to which its main door opens, an axis marked out by the little water channel of its fountain or central spout. The entrance to the chamber is now from the Patio del León. It can be noted here that Alphonse XI was one of the first Castilian monarchs whose love of hunting is recorded, and the *Libro de la Montería* was written at his command from 1342-1350. This is a codex which may have been illustrated in the very Alcázares of Seville.

The name of the room alludes to the throne which formerly stood adjoining the wall and from where Pedro I imparted justice. Pedro had his step-brother, Fadrique, Master of the Order of Santiago, killed in this room, according to popular legend accused of adultery with the queen. In function, this room corresponds to the *maswar* or *mexuar* of Moorish palaces. The Patio del Yeso is one of the few remaining elements from the old Almohade palace. A quadran-

Chamfered coffering in the Chamber of Justice.

gular courtyard of small dimensions, it originally featured two identical galleries facing each other across the longer sides of the patio, the shorter sides being unadorned. The arcade which has been conserved has three spaces divided by strong pillars, the central space occupied by a great arch of lambrequins, its squinches decorated with sebka (ornamental mouldings forming meshes of rhomboids). At the sides is a triple arcade supported by two columns with Caliphal capitals over whose arches panels embroidered with sebka. This three-sided design of the arcades and their arrangement in the patio formed the starting-point of a long series of Moorish and Mudéjar patios, among which we can mention that of Los Arrayanes in the Alhambra and that of Las Doncellas in the

Patio del Yeso.

Alcázar itself. Inside the galleries are portals giving access to the rooms of the Almohade Palacio del Yeso, their structure and decoration reminiscent of Cordoban art, particularly the doors of the Medina Azahara. The southern entrance gives access to a large room with alcoves at the sides, in which can be observed fragments of Mudéjar paintings and others from the time of the Catholic Monarchs. The remains of the patio and adjoining palace were discovered by Tubino in 1885 and were restored according to the criteria laid down by the Marquis of La Vega Inclán by José Gómez Otero and José Gómez Millán between 1918 and 1920.

Casa de la Contratación and Cuarto del Almirante

The Casa de la Contratación was founded in 1503, occupying the rooms until then used as Admiralty courts, on the site of the palace rebuilt by the Almohades in the western section of the Reales Alcázares. The Catholic Monarchs were in no doubt that this important institution, whose main function was to control merchant traffic with the Indies and which soon took over powers concerning scientific matters resulting from the discovery of America, and navigation, should be situated within their palace in Seville, particularly for reasons of control and security, as the Casa de la Contratación received much of the treasure brought to Spain from the New World.

Room I. Holy Week Procession (19th century).

Sala II, or Room of the Admiral.

ROOM I

Three rooms belonging to the original building can be visited. The first contains a collection of Sevillian tiles from the 19th and 20th centuries. These were produced by the workshops of Ramos Rejano, the Mensaque family and Manuel Corbato (Adoration of the Monarchs, 1897) and form a small sample of one of the city's most flourishing crafts since medieval times, revitalised in the 19th century when historians like José Gestoso helped to create the designs used. Also displayed is a surprising large painting depicting the Procession of El Santo Entierro Grande, with detailed reproduction of the *pasos,* or floats, nazarenos and members of the procession, insignia, public and urban scenes. This is an anonymous work from the mid-19th century.

ROOM II

Known as the Sala del Almirante due to its original function as the seat of the Castilian Admiralty, this room contains an important collection of portraits of real people and others depicting historic scenes, all the property of the National Heritage Commission except the first-mentioned:

Las Postrimerías de San Fernando: by the Sevillian painter Virgilio Mattoni (1887, Prado Museum collection), this work represents the death of King Ferdinand III in the Alcázar of Seville according to the description which his son, the Wise King, gives in his «Estoria de España»: «And when the King saw that his affliction grew in just a few days and understood that the last hour was coming, and that everlasting life in heaven was coming to him, he had Don Remondo and other

«The Storming of Loja», by Eusebio Valldeperas (1862). (Patrimonio Nacional).

bishops and archbishops come, and all the clergy, and that they should bring his the Body of God... And when he felt it come, he let himself fall from the bed. And, overcome, he took a piece of rope and tied it around his neck... and asking God's pardon and affirming his belief in the truth of the Holy Church, he received the Body of God from the hands of the said Don Remondo, Archbishop of Seville».

The Taking of Loja in 1486 by Ferdinand the Catholic, painted in 1862 by Eusebio Valldeperas, a work presented at the National Fine Art Exhibition in the same year. In it, the last Nasrite king of Granada, Boabdil (Abd-Allah el Zaquir) surrenders the keys to the city in presence of Gonzalo Fernández of Córdoba, known as El Gran Capitán.

Portrait of **Saint Francis of Assisi,** regent king by marriage with Isabel II, by Bernardo López (1864).

Portraits of **Ferdinand VII** and his fourth wife, **Maria Cristina of Naples,** by Carlos Blanco in the first third of the 19th century.

Portraits of **Louis Philip of Orleans,** king of France, and his wife, **Maria Amalia,** and of their children **Antonio** and **Luisa Fernanda of Bourbon,** Duchess of Montpensier, by Franz Xaver Winterhalter (1845).

These are magnificent examples of 19th-century courtly portraits. All four are from the Palace of Miramar in San Sebastian.

Presiding over the room is the painting by Alfonso Grosso of the **Opening of the Ibero-American Exhibition in Seville** on 9 May 1929 by King Alphonse XIII and Queen Victoria Eugenia of Battenberg. The painting shows a gallery of portraits of the royal family and personalities from political and military life in which the following can be recognised: on the right, infantas Cristina and Beatriz next to their brother, Prince Alphonse and their uncle Carlos of Bourbon; on the left, generals Berenguer and Primo de Rivera, the Marquis of Nervión and, at the end, closing the group, José Calvo Sotelo.

«The Opening of the Ibero-American Exhibition in Seville», by Alfonso Grosso. (Patrimonio Nacional).

Altarpiece of the Madonna of Seafarers, by Alejo Fernández (16th century).

(Patrimonio Nacional).

ROOM III

Chapel or Chapterhouse

This is a room with a square groundplan designed for the meetings of officials and cosmographs from the Casa de la Contratación, and to this end there is a stone bench around the walls. Presiding over the room is the Altarpiece of the Madonna of Seafarers, a work by Alejo Fernández (1531-1536) painted, ex professo, for installation here. The work portrays some of the first discoverers and promoters of colonisation: Christopher Columbus, the Pinzón brothers, the Catholic Monarchs and, in the background, indigenous Americans protected under the mantle of the Virgin. Depicted in the lower section, we can observe a wide range of vessels from the period: caravels, galleys and launches. The central panel is flanked by four smaller ones representing Saint John the Evangelist, Saint Telmo, the Apostle James and Saint Sebastian. The roof of the chapel features magnificent 16th-century coffering whose octagonal starry coffers trace the cross of Saint John, under which is stucco work featuring typical Renaissance motifs. The walls are decorated with fifteen reposteros featuring the coats of arms of the admirals of Castile from 1254 to 1492. The coat of arms of Christopher Columbus is opposite the altarpiece. In the western wall, a window opens over the series of patios which adjoined or formed part of the former Casa del Asistente: the Patio de Romero Murube and the Patio de los Levíes.

In 1967, large-scale restoration work was carried out here, consisting of the rebuilding of the perimeter bench, the installation of the present floor, the carving of the new altarpiece to house the paintings in imitation of the original, lost during the 19th century, and the decoration of the walls with the embroidered cloths representing coats of arms.

In the western gallery of the Patio de la Montería, entered from the Cuarto del Almirante, is a commemorative plaque installed on the occasion of the visit of Charles IV in 1796, placed here by the Royal Academy of Science, which reads: «Carolo IV et Aloisiae conjugi Hispalim adventu suo Beantibus Regia Scientiarum Academia optimis atque optatissimis Regibus dedicavit. III kal. mart. Anno MDCCXCVI».

Gallery and entrance to the Room of the Admiral.

Patio del Asistente. ▷

Patios of El Asistente, Levíes and Romero Murube

The house of the city *asistente* was built in this zone in the 18th century. The centre of the site is formed by a Castilian-style patio, restored in 1967. The ground floor has ten Tuscan columns whose capitals support broad wooden footings which, in turn, sustain the beams on which the floor of the upper gallery rests. This formula is repeated in the upper gallery, though the columns are replaced by bevelled studding. The heads of the beams form rows of corbels supporting the eaves of the building. This patio, which now appears remote from the Sevillian architecture of the Siglo de Oro, is a good example of the many similar patios which may have existed in the city, designed according to the Castilian Mudéjar style, a determining influence in certain zones of the palace. Unfortunately, the fragility of these wooden structures make this a rare example of the type to have survived. The building currently houses a collection of tiles from the Alcázar demonstrating a varied range of techniques (dry cord, lipped edged, flat, etc) and styles from late-Gothic through the Renaissance work of Niculoso Pisano to the Modernist designs of the late-19th century.

This main patio is complemented by two smaller courtyards, that of Los Levíes and that of Romero Murube. The first takes its name from the lovely Mannerist porch or loggia which occupies one of its front walls and which was brought here from the House of Los Levíes, a palace now lost which formerly stood in the Jewish quarter of the city. It was installed here in 1969. Its four arches rest on three small veined

Chapel. Admiral's Room.

Patio de los Levíes. ▷

marble columns whose height is increased by their supports of rectangular podia and their prolongation in plate rails. The side arches are supported by pilasters built into the wall. The Mannerist taste for contrasts of volume, effects of light and shade and the playful will to surprise are exemplified in this loggia, where the supports are made lighter, the masses of the spandrels open up in oculos and the central podium is transformed into a fountain whose four spouts in the form of lions' heads, fill with water the central pond.
The third patio, that of Romero Murube, or of Los Poetas, is thus known in memory and tribute to the curator of these Reales Alcázares from 1934 to 1969 and who described himself as «an apprentice gardener in one of the most noble orchards in the world». In his memory, the atmosphere of a tiny Andalusian patio has been recreated here, so much loved by the poet who saw in this modest domestic element the origin of the finest Sevillian gardens.

Mudéjar Palace
It was King Pedro I who ordered the construction of a new palace in the Reales Alcázares, using the remains of the old 11th-century Abbadite Alcázar. The palace, built between 1364 and 1366, is the finest example of Mudéjar civil architecture and employs a formal language very close to that of Islamic art, superbly combining Toledan and Sevillian Mudéjar with the Nasrite style, for part of the work was carried out by master builders from sent Granada by Sultan Muhammed V to his ally, the Castilian king, along with Sevillian craftsmen who continued the Almohade tradition and the workshops of Toledan plasterers and carpenters, whose masters mixed Christian and Moorish decorative motifs. This is, therefore, both functionally and decoratively an Islamic palace in which the different spaces were organised according to their intended use, public or private. In it are differentiated a domestic area from a Royal Chamber and a series of representational spaces which interlink scenographically and culminate in the Salón de Embajadores. The decoration, too, is imbued with Moorish concepts and forms.

The Islamic liturgy, with its mechanised rituals and repetitive orations creates rhythms of space and time which influence Moorish architecture. The multiplication of identical elements in infinite patterns are the image of the limitless divinity. Religious concepts are introduced into daily life and such ideas are imposed as the palace-paradise, the celestial dwelling-place which the powerful tried to build on earth. The Alcázar of the Moorish princes of Al-Andalus and, possibly, that of the Castilian monarchs who imitated them, partake of this vision of Eden. The gardens and fountains, the exultant decoration covering walls, roofs and pavements, everything anticipates images which Koranic descriptions of the after-life vividly depict.

Inscription on the founding of the Palace of Rey Don Pedro.

Palace façade.

I. FAÇADE

The visitor's gaze is drawn to and focussed on the great façade, a palpable demonstration of the magnificence and power of the sovereign who ordered it built. In it are coordinated the three tendencies we have already mentioned, the Granadan, the Sevillian and the Toledan. The play of volumes is completely successful, the generally horizontal nature of the whole being compensated for by the vertical space of the central panel, where the finest decoration is centred and which is prolonged above the two lines of eaves in the roof of the square audience chamber on the upper floor. In the central space, the sculpted stone, ceramic, carved wood and brick all combine together, though installed separately by master builders of differing decorative traditions. The lower section, where the ashlars contribute to the chromatic effect with their slight pillowing, are divided into three lanes. In the central part there is a door, whose lintel is formed by richly carved voussoirs, adorned with naturalistic floral motifs in the Toledan style. The side lanes are occupied by cusped blind arches resting on columns with Caliphal capitals brought from elsewhere and featuring a delicate work of sebka clearly inspired by the nearby Giralda. In the second section, the side lanes repeated the pattern of the lower part, multiplying the tiny cusped arches whose interior is decorated with fine reliefs in Cufic epigraphy amongst the floral motifs. The arches support the sebka work, which includes the heraldic emblems of the king: castles, lions and the coat of arms of the Order of the Band. The central section, separated from the others by geometric ceramic friezes of tiles, repeats the floral and heraldic decoration in another relief, this time less sharp. Over this second space opens the main structure, with three arches in the central ajimez and two at either end. The columns are made of marble and have Moorish capitals, the pendentive arch delimited by the frieze decorated with ceramic ornate motifs. Over these spaces is situated in the form of a lintel a double inscription, the central in Arabic, inscribed on cobalt blue and white tiles which, in rectangular Cufic letters repeats the Nasrite motto «Wa la Galiba Illa-llah» («And there is no victor but Allah») eight times. Surrounding this inscription, in Gothic letters, is the following text: «EL MUY ALTO ET MUY NOBLE ET MUY PODEROSO ET MUY CONQUERIDO DON PEDRO POR LA GRACIA DE DIOS REY DE CASTIELLA ET DE LEON MANDO FAÇER ESTOS ALCAZARES ET ESTOS PALAÇIOS ET ESTAS PORTADAS QUE FUE FECHO EN LA ERA DE MIL+ET DE CUATROÇIENTOS DOS» («The high, noble, powerful and beloved Pedro, by the grace of God king of Castile and Leon, ordered these Alcázares, palaces and gates built in 1402»). This façade, then, dates back to the year 1402 in the Hispanic era, or 1364 AD. The entire façade is crowned by a broad wooden eave, carved in the Toledan style. Between the two large modillions is a mocarab frieze, all formerly gilt.

Vestibule of the Palace of Rey Don Pedro.

II. THE PUBLIC AREA

Vestibule

The palace vestibule has an elbowed shape, following the Islamic tradition, by this arrangement concealing the view of the central courtyard. This shape and the absence of openings give this patio a dark, shadowy atmosphere which is immediately and surprisingly dispelled when we reach the light and open space of the huge Patio de las Doncellas. Taking the official, or public route, we enter the Palace, turning left, whilst the private route leads from a narrow corridor opening up on the right to the Patio de las Muñecas, centre of the Royal Apartments or domestic area of the Mudéjar palace.

From the palace entrance, we come to a first space, in the shape of a long rectangle divided into three parts by stilted arches richly adorned with plasterwork, resting on columns whose roughly-carved capitals are Visigoth in origin, possibly having been brought here from the former Basilica of San Vicente in the Patio de Banderas. The side spaces are covered in Mudéjar panelled ceilings whose geometric pattern forms eight-pointed stars. The central panels and the tile socles (1905) are modern. In 1805, a door was opened giving direct access to the Patio de las Doncellas, crossing the Royal Chamber and in this way creating an axis contrary to the spirit of the building.

The room forming an angle to the left, with 15th-century coffering, gives way to the short, narrow corridor, reached through an arch whose arrabá moulding is decorated with Toledan stucco work (14th century). The passageway is covered with a vault and others over Almohade elephant trunks, surviving vestiges of the original 12th-century Alcázar. Below them is an epigraphic inscription. On the left is the beginning of the staircase known as the Escalera de las Damas which, in several flights, communicated with the upper floor of the Mudéjar palace, the Gothic palace and the Patio de la Montería. Originally, this corridor and staircase formed part of an Almohade gate of elbowed disposition which gave access to the first rooms of the Alcázar or Dar Al Imara.

Arches in the Patio de las Doncellas.

Patio de las Doncellas

This splendid courtyard forms the centre of the Palace of Pedro I. It is a masterpiece of Mudéjar art, rectangular in shape with galleries on both floors, the lower corresponding to the 14th century, greatly altered in the 16th, when the upper arcade was built. The shorter sides of the patio feature five cusped arches supporting double columns, the central of which is wider and higher than the others, reaching up to the eave crowing the lower gallery. The same formula is followed with the longer sides, though this time with seven arches. The double columns used to replace the original supports as part of the restoration carried out in the 16th century are made of marble from the Genoan workshops of Antonio María Aprile de Caronna. Over the side arches is a delicate sebka

Patio de las Doncellas: entrance to the Royal Chamber.

Tiles in the Salón de Embajadores (of the ambassadors).

work in which Toledo and Granada stucco work show the range of decorative forms used in Moorish art. From the symbolic hand of Fatima spring alauriques, palmettes, pineapples, veneras, all framed by Moorish epigraphy. During the alterations carried out during the Renaissance period, the coat of arms of the emperor were added to the squinches of the arches, whilst balustrades and inscriptions were added to the pilasters. In the inner face of the pillar in the southwest corner, between the Salón de Embajadores and the Sala del Techo de Carlos V, an inscription bears the name of the architect responsible for the work, and the date of the same: «Francisco Martínez M°. 1569 A».

The tiled socles date back to the 14th century and feature highly original decorative motifs, some of them resembling those used in the Alhambra. The panelled ceilings, with eight-starred ornamental work are from the times of the Catholic Monarchs, poorly restored in 1856. Some of the veined shafts of the little columns of the ajimeces were brought here, according to the records, from the palace of the King of Aragon in Valencia by the troops of Pedro I on their return from the war between the two kingdoms.

The upper gallery was built between 1540 and 1572 according to the design of architect Luis de Vega. The four fronts are articulated by semicircular arches resting on marble columns alternately double or simple and triple in the corners. They are supported by a balustrade whose pillars are decorated with the motto of the emperor, the Plus Ultra and the columns of Hercules. In the spandrels of the arches and friezes, the original Renaissance stucco work which formerly adorned them has been reconstructed, featuring such classical themes as the emperor and his wife, Isabel of Portugal wearing laurel crowns, coats of arms and mottoes, roleos, candalieri and putti. The restoration work is by Rafael Manzano between 1983 and 1987, altering the space of the upper platforms by blocking the eastern corridor with a partition decorated with plasterwork imitating Mudéjar models.

Salón de Embajadores

The centre of the public area is made up by this Chamber of the Ambassadors, or throne room, the space where the king gave audience and the scene of such historic events as the marriage of Emperor Charles with Isabel of Portugal. This space, with a square groundplan and covered by a wooden dome of Moorish traceria, responds to Islamic architecture of the Qubba with formal precedents and use as the sala de solio in Hispano-Moorish art in the Caliphal palace of Medina Azahara. Recent studies show that its structure of walls, columns and arches corresponds to the Al-Turayya (the Pleiades) room of the Abbadite Palace of Al Mutamid (11th century), all of it redecorated and its orientation changed to face the Patio de las Doncellas during the reign of King Pedro I. The entrance doorway is a magnificent example of Mudéjar carpintry, in larch wood, with lattice-work motifs forming 12-pointed stars, responding to the

Entrance to the Salón de Embajadores.

Salón de Embajadores.

type known as *gorronera,* as, open, they formed a veritable decorative tapestry covering the walls which open onto the patio. In the lower part are two wickets in the shape of horseshoe arches. Each leaf is surrounded by an Arabic inscription on the outer face and Spanish the inner. The Arabic inscription reads: «Our Lord the Sultan, made great, elevated, Don Pedro, King of Castile and Leon (may Allah perpetuate his happiness and that of his architect) these doors were made of carved wood for this apartment of joy (which he ordered in honour and grandeur of the noble and brave ambassadors) of which springs forth in abundance happiness for this blessed city, in which were built the palaces and alcazares; and these mansions are for my Lord and master, the only thing which gave life to his splendour, the pious, generous Sultan, who ordered it built in the city of Seville, with the help of his intercessor with God the Father. In its dazzling construction and embellishment happiness sprang forth; in its work, Toledan artifices were used; and this was the ennobled year 1404 (1366 AD), similar to the afternoon twilight and most like to the firiness of the twilight of the aurora is this work. A throne, shining in bright colours and intense splendour. Praise be to Allah». These incriptions date the work to 1366, affirming that it was carried out by Toledan Mudéjars, as well as naming the room the Sala de la Felicidad or de los Embajadores. In the interior, in large Gothic characters are reproduced the beginning of the Gospel According to Saint John and passages from the 53rd Psalm *(salvum me fact in virtute...).*

Dome in the Salón de Embajadores.

View of the Galería de Reyes, Diego de Esquivel.
(Patrimonio Nacional).

Salón de Embajadores: balconies, stucco and mocarabs.

The interior of the Salón de Embajadores features the most sumptuous and delicate decoration of the entire Mudéjar palace. Springing from the complex tile-covered socles, in which tiny multi-coloured pieces of ceramic form starred patterns, lattice-work and undulating designs whose roots lie with the art of the Granadan Nasrites, the walls are decorated with Arabesques, atauriques and epigraphy in gilt and painted stucco forming a lower section of four great blind arches featuring on three sides elegant Moorish arches supported by Caliphal columns. Over a frieze of 44 small arches in which, once more, appear the heraldic emblems of Castile and Leon, four wrought-iron balconies open up, the work of Francisco López, installed here between 1592 and 1597. Higher up is the gallery featuring representations of the Castilian monarchs from the time of the Goths to Philip III, 56 panels painted in the late-16th century by Diego de Esquivel (1599-1600). Over them, in the frieze in the dome, are 32 busts of ladies, probably portraits of queens and princesses. The entire work is crowned by the great Mudéjar dome, whose starting-point is a 12-pointed star and which rests on mocarab trunks. This is the work of Diego Ruiz in 1427, as was certified in 1843 when one of his panels was found, bearing the following inscription: «Maestro Mayor del Rey Don Diego Roiz made me... and this series was made in the month of August in the Year of Our Lord 1427» replacing the old panels from the times of Al-Mutamid and King Pedro I.

Coffering in the Sala del Techo de Philip II.

Sala del Techo de Felipe II

In terms of length, this is one of the largest rooms on the ground floor. It forms part of the series of rooms for official use surrounding the Salón de Embajadores. It is known as the Sala de Media Caña or Sala del Techo de Felipe II as its coffering dates back to the reign of Philip II, installed between 1589 and 1591, attributed to master carpenter Martín Infante. An outstanding example of Mannerist coffering, this is made up of square coffers forming simple cruciform and quadrangular patterns, their slight curve the signature of the likely author. The main work of art in this room is the arch giving access to the Salón de Embajadores, its peacock decoration making it known as the Arco de Pavones. Originally, it formed the main entrance to the throne room of the Abaddite kings (11th century) and still conserves from this period the columns with their Caliphal capitals. The rich plasterwork is, however, from the 14th century, and includes the most original demonstration of Mudéjar motifs: atauriques, Moorish epigraphy, starred lattices, geometrically-arranged balloons, veneras, all Moorish in origin, along with vines, scrolls and the flat silhouettes of eagles and other birds, combining Christian motifs with themes from Persian art, including peacocks in the arch spandrels. Finally, other features include the socle of Mudéjar tiles and the original floor partially conserved in the room. Lined with tiles and stone, it was restored in 1896 by José Gómez Otero with ceramic pieces from the works of the Jiménez brothers.

Original entrance to the Salón de Embajadores. Arch of Peacocks.

The Salón de Embajadores seen from the adjoining room.

Rooms adjacent to the Salón de Embajadores

Communicating with the Salón de Embajadores and the Sala del Techo de Felipe II, these two apartments complete the area reserved by protocol for royal receptions and the public life of the monarch. The coffered ceilings are attributed to Martín Infante (1590-1598), whilst the most interesting feature of the decoration of the two rooms are the cut plaster plaques forming medallions decorated with the silhouettes of kings, knights, ladies and fantastic animals taking us back to the medieval world and its legends and popular tales. The plasterwork also features decorative motifs from Gothic art. The exact meaning of these silhouettes has been much discussed and debated, though that they date back to the 14th century is clear from the clothes worn by the figures. Some historians believe there is a narrative purpose behind them and that they allude to the texts and illustrations of the Trojan Chronicles, a book written and illuminated in around 1350. These tell tales of knightly valour, jousting, the storming of castles, sea voyages, the rescue of ladies and combat with fantastic animals, themes much to the liking of kings Alphonse I and Pedro I, who respectively founded and continued the Knightly Order of the Band.

Plasterwork in the Salón de Embajadores.

Room of the Ceiling of Carlos V.

III. Private Area (Rooms of the Royal Family)

Rooms of the Princes and Princesses

The private apartments of the royal family, used during the summer, adjoined the north and south sides of the Patio de las Doncellas. On the southern flank, their windows opening over the Garden of the Galera, are two series of rooms, a group of three known as the Rooms of the Princes and Princesses, and, adjoining these, the great Sala del Techo de Felipe II, used as a chapel during the 16th century.

The Rooms of the Princes and Princesses are arranged according to a traditional model of Hispano-Moslim art: a larger, rectangular central space on whose shorter sides are two almost square rooms, used as alcoves in the princely residence. Unfortunately, during the 19th century, these rooms were reorganised, with the loss of their character, the plasterwork changed and the original spaces replaced by «Morisco» windows. In the central room, a marble plaque commemorates the birth here of the daughter of the Duke and Duchess of Monpensier: «In this room was born on 21 September 1848 HRH the Infanta of Spain, Doña María Isabel of Orleans and Bourbon». The western of these rooms communicates with the Sala del Techo de Felipe II, the eastern with both the Patio de las Doncellas and the Sala del Techo de Felipe II.

◁ *Rooms of the Infantes.*

Detail of the Charles V ceiling.

Sala del Techo de Felipe II (Chapel)

This room in the palace of King Pedro I was used for domestic purposes and therefore repeats the compositional scheme of separating two areas by an arch, the smaller used as an *alhania,* or alcove, which could be isolated from the rest of the room by curtains. The room was later converted into a chapel, the alcove forming the presbytery, and features fine Mudéjar decoration with friezes, plasterwork and carved woodwork in doors and Moorish windows. The little columns of the windows are Moorish. The outer face of the arch giving access to the Patio de las Doncellas is surrounded by a Eucharistic inscription indicating the religious use to which this space was put. This is, in fact, a prayer attributed to Saint Buenaventura and which in those times formed part of the devotional texts used by priests before the celebration of mass.

The coffering of the ceiling was installed between 1541 and 1543 during the reign of Emperor Charles, and is attributed to Sebastián de Segovia. It forms one of the finest examples of Spanish Renaissance ceiling work. Inspired by models composed by the Italian tratadista Sebastiano Serlio, it is made up of richly-moulded octagonal coffers which leave between them smaller square spaces. The centre of the coffers is decorated with floral pendants, except for 13 in the central area, which feature carved busts of knights, elderly gentlemen and ladies, in allusion to Charles V and his wife, Isabel of Portugal. The frieze on the ceiling features imperial coats of arms, the emblem of the Plus Ultra and Renaissance motifs: gargoyles, scrolls, roleos and putti. Below are 16th-century plasterwork pieces.

Royal Apartment

The main section of the private area of the palace was situated on the north side of the Patio de las Doncellas, where the king and queen's chambers were located around a small domestic patio, that of Las Muñecas.

Royal Chamber and Alcove

The Royal Chamber and Alcove, popularly known as the Dormitory of the Moorish Kings, is reached from the Patio de las Doncellas through a large stilted semicircular arch, over which open three windows with whitewashed plaster lattices which feature Arabic inscriptions and palmettes. This entrance has carved doors of Mudéjar lattice-work, restored various times during different periods, with beautiful lintels over which their hinges rotate. In the same wall are two Moorish windows framed by Mudéjar plasterwork with Caliphal capitals. Entrance archway, lattices and windows allow light and air to enter the first room, or Royal Chamber, a space of transition between the king's public activities and his private life, for which the second room, or Alcove, was reserved. This distinction between functions does not prevent the structure of the two rooms from being identical, however, rectangular spaces in which a fine pointed arch opens up an alcove. The two sections are communicated by three Moorish arches whose design is reminiscent of Caliphal art. The decoration of both rooms features Mudéjar plasterwork and with a tiled covering alternating with 19th-century imitations. The coffered ceiling combines starred lattice-work with Renaissance coffering. The Alcove still bears the marks of the access opened up in 1805 by the architect Manuel Cintora to create direct communication between the main entrance and the Patio de las Doncellas. During the restoration work of 1856, this door was closed up again, and the original elbowed entrance was restored. The royal alcove also features the ancient Caliphal base, bearing an Arabic inscription, on one of the columns of the alcove arch.

Sala de Pasos Perdidos

From the Royal Chamber, we reach the Patio de las Muñecas through a small square-shaped room, known as that of the Pasos Perdidos. The Arabesques and friezes of the spaces of this «Room of the Lost Steps» are decorated with 14th-century plasterwork in Sevillian style (sebka, palmettes and ataurique), later reformed, as can be seen from the addition of the Cross of Saint John in the interior of some of the lattices. The ceiling is coffered, dating back to the time of the Catholic Monarchs.

Patio de las Muñecas

This is a tiny courtyard, the image and model of so many little domestic Sevillian patios. The harmonious equilibrium of its volumes, with the assymetric solution of its arcades and the delicacy with which it is decorated, make this one of the architectural jewels of the entire palace. One can only lament that the 19th century Romantic movement, with its insistence on «embellishing» monuments and palaces, should have so radically altered the upper floors. The restorer, Rafael Contreras, director of the Alhambra alterations, indiscriminately copied plasterwork and ornaments from that palace, covering the patio with a glass roof.

The ground floor is original, dating to the 14th century, articulating its ten arches with Caliphal marble columns alternately black, white and pink. There are four major arches feature fine ataurique work in their jambs, whilst there are panels of sebka over the minor arches and over the line of the *alfiz* there runs a frieze of small lobular arches.

This lower floor bears witness to the work of Moorish craftsmen sent from Granada by Muhammad V to decorate the palace of his friend, King Pedro. There are original plaster pieces bearing the Nasrite motto, and some of the tiles are reminiscent of those in the Alhambra. The columns and their capitals, featuring climbing plants, are older, dating to the 10th century and brought here by Al-Mutamid from the Medina Azahara.

It is said that the name of this patio («of the dolls») is due to the four small heads which appear in the plasterwork at the beginning of the arch situated in the corner closest to the corridor leading to the vestibule.

Sala del Techo de los Reyes Católicos

This is a square-shaped room symmetrical to that of Los Pasos Perdidos. The main entrance is from the western gallery of the Patio de las Muñecas, and it communicates with the Sala del Techo de Felipe II. The restoration work carried out during the 19th century included the opening up of the Moorish window which looks onto the Garden of El Principe. The plasterwork of the broad frieze and the Arabesques of the doors are Mudéjar. The main feature of this room is its ceiling, 12-pointed lattice-work frieze dating back to the times of the Catholic Monarchs. The arrocabe bears the coats of arms and mottoes of the two monarchs: the escutcheon of the crowns of Castile and Aragon over the Eagle of Saint John, and shields bearing the bundle of arrows, the yoke with the rope and the motto «Tanto Monta». The pomegranate which appears on the shields and painted panels painted with Renaissance motifs «a candelieri» date this work after 1492, and it was probably carried out in the early 16th century. We know nothing of the original function of this room during the times of King Pedro, though, from its situation, we can see that it is a space of transition between the domestic area and the institutional spaces around the Salón de Embajadores.

Bevelled coffering in the Prince's Room.

Prince's Room, or Queen's Dormitory

We conclude our visit to the ground floor of the Mudéjar palace by admiring this room in the private area. Its traditional name, that of the «Prince's Room», allows us to suppose that it was, at least from the 14th century onwards, the queen's alcove and that it was here, therefore, that Prince John, frustrated heir to the Catholic Monarchs, was born.

The room is divided into three sections by large arches resting on pillars, with the habitual alcoves at either end. The ceilings are coffered in the alcoves with a frieze in the central space. The coffering of the western side is particularly interesting, the work of Juan de Simancas in 1543 and a fine example of 16th-century Sevillian carpentry. It is made up of large coffers separated by mouldings, whose interior is decorated with Mudéjar motifs of lattice work and pineapples. In the opposite alcove, the coffering is octagonal over mocarab trunks, its lattice work starting from an eight-pointed star and the painted decoration including much-restored Renaissance masks and scrolls.

The windows of this room were opened up in 1805 during the reforms carried out by Manuel Cintora. The ceilings and plasterwork were restored in 1833 and then again in 1855-1856.

◁ *Patio de las Muñecas.*

◁ *Prince's room.*

Patio del Crucero, or of María de Padilla.

Patio del Crucero and Gothic Palace

Patio

Also known as the Patio of María de Padilla or of Carlos V, the present appearance of this patio bears little resemblance to its original aspect when it was built by the Almohade sultans in the 12th century. The Moorish patio was slightly altered as part of the works carried out during the reign of Alphonse X, the Wise, in order to build the Gothic Palace of the Alcázar, but the alterations which definitively modified its form were carried out by the military engineer Sebastián Van de Borsch after the site was damaged by the famous Lisbon earthquake of 1755. This explains the 18th-century look of the site, between late-baroque and the academicist tendencies which led to neoclassicism. Constructed during this time were the columned porch and the entrance to Gothic Palace, misnamed the Salones de Carlos V, and the gallery which joins the Apeadero to the Patio de la Montería, and from which the patio which concerns us now is reached.

Nevertheless, the original patio is conserved almost intact, buried under the gardened platforms and cultivated plots and reached from the Garden of the Dance. Its original structure was that of a patio-garden with two planes of elevation. The lower, subterranean or summer garden, was made up of the four plots which separated two galleries in the form of a cross, in which orange and lemons trees were planted. The higher level was made up of the flat roofs of the cruciform galleries and the perimeter galleries. All this

Underground pond and garden of the Patio del Crucero, or of María de Padilla.

resulted in one of the most original and functional elements of Hispano-Muslim art. During the hot months, the lower garden, with its trees, the porches of its galleries and great central pond was the ideal spot for walking and resting in the shade. On cold days, the higher platforms, with ceramic-covered handrails, was a veritable solarium with the added attraction of having orange flowers and fruits within arm's reach.

The design of this patio used to astonish visitors to the Royal Palace, as we can see from the testimony of Venetian ambassador Andrea Navaggiero during his stay as a guest at the wedding of Emperor Charles in 1526: «there are baths and rooms and various chambers through all of which passes water through strange artifices, and these are truly delicious spots in summer; there is a patio full of the most beautiful orange and lemon trees, and inside are more peaceful gardens and an orange grove where the sun cannot penetrate, perhaps the most peaceful site in the whole of Spain». Years later, in 1634, the Sevillian historian and scholar Rodrigo Caro bequeathed us a lovely description of the patio: «From here one enters another patio known as the Crucero, due to its cross-like shape, and, though you enter on a level plane, below you is an underground garden with orange trees, divided into four parts, so deep compared to this patio that the tops of the trees barely reach this height. This Crucero is formed by robust arches of brick and mortar, with whitewashed buttresses here and there, between which is a great pool of water runs underneath, the length of the Crucero above, and on

Lantern of the Tapestry Room.

either side of this garden are corridors supporting the platforms, and corridors in the patio above, all of which is beautifully carved with handrails on either side, covered with tiles, beginning at a fount of marble, where there is a waterfall, harmoniously surrounded by white marble. This patio is, then, with its beautiful view of the sky above and its extraordinary structure and the views of the garden below, a cheerful, spacious place, and as regards the underground garden, in summer it is the shadiest and freshest place one could hope to imagine».

Tapestry Room

This Salón de Tapices is the first room in the old Gothic Palace, known, along with the next described in this guide, as the Salas de las Fiestas. Ruined by the earthquake of 1755, it was completely rebuilt by Sebastián Van der Borsch. Elements pertaining to the new design are the five vaults recently decorated with mouldings and royal coats of arms, as well as the lantern which lights the central area and the flat brackets in which the arches culminate. It was in these rooms that the festivities for the wedding of Charles V and Isabel of Portugal probably took place. Another interesting feature are the Renaissance grilles made from designs by Asensio de Maeda (1578-1579).

The room is now hung with six tapestries pertaining to the National Heritage, which form part of the series of twelve commissioned by Philip V and woven by Francisco and Cornelio Van der Gotten at the Royal Tapestry Factories in Madrid and Seville during the

Tapestry Room.

Tapestry in the series entitled «The Conquest of Tunis», number 1. (Patrimonio Nacional).

second quarter of the 18th century. These copy the designs of the series on the conquest of Tunis, original 16th-century tapestries designed by Dutch painters Jan Vermayen and Pieter de Coeck van Aelst and made in the workshops of Guillermo Pannemaker between 1548 and 1554, ten of which are conserved in the Palacio Real in Madrid.

The scenes narrating the military campaign in Tunis are framed by a complex Renaissance orla in whose corners are the imperial coat of arms and the cross of Burgundy. In the centre of the left-hand side is the motto «Plus Oultre» between the columns of Hercules. In the upper and lower friezes, the events are depicted in cards, with the text in Spanish, above, and in Latin, below.

On the right-hand side, another smaller card enumerates the different tapestries, giving information about the landscapes represented in them. They vary in size between 560 x 712 cm in the case of Number 11 to 583 x 981 cm in that of Number 12.

The six tapestries currently exhibited in the Alcázar are as follows:

I: Map of the Western Mediterranean, showing the Iberian Peninsula and the African coast. This tapestry opens the series, showing the geographical setting of the campaign. The map is inverted, as the cartela explains, in order to emphasise the Tunisian coastline in which the campaign took place in the upper section of the piece. On the right is a self-portrait by Jan Vermayen, artist and narrator of the series.

II: Inspection of the troops in Barcelona. The scene depicts the Spanish and Portugues troops parading in preparation for boarding ship in the port of Barcelona, portrayed in the background. The equestrian

Tapestry in the series «The Conquest of Tunis», number 2. (Patrimonio Nacional).

figure of Emperor Charles, who looks out at the viewer from the right of the picture, is followed by various knights including the emperor's brother-in-law, Prince Louis of Portugal.

IX and X: The conquest and sacking of Tunis. These two drapes form a single unit as they depict how the city was overrun and sacked by the Imperial troops. Tapestry IX (originally on the right-hand side) represents the military operations of the Christian army, whilst Number X (left) shows the surrender of the city. In the centre, Charles V frees two Christian captives, whilst the painter Jan Vermayen appears in the midground taking notes from real life. In the background is an overall view of Tunis.

XI: The army camps at Rada. The painter concentrates on the subject of the background scene, where the emperor, on horseback, leads his troops out of the city of Tunis, heading for Rada, where they boarded ship. In the foreground is depicted a costumbrist scene, full of exoticism, in which Christian musketeers accompany a host of Moors come to supply the fleet with vituals. Examples of African fauna are also depicted.

XII: The returning troops embark at La Goleta. In this tapestry, which closes the series, we see the fortress of La Goleta with artillery, and the signing of the surrender by Muley Hasssan, king of Tunisia, before the Emperor Charles. Together with these scenes, the painter also entertains himself by narrating anecdotes showing the disasters of war and the life of the troops. In the background are the galleys and ships which take the soldiers to their various destinations.

Sala de los Azulejos (Room of the Tiles).

Busts of the Emperor Charles V and Isabel of Portugal in the Sala de los Azulejos, by Cristóbal de Augusta (16th century).

Tile Room

This Sala de Azulejos, parallel to the room described previously, still conserves its five Gothic vaults, built in the time of Alphonse X (13th century). The room is reached through the Tapestry Room, its great spaces between flying buttreses overlooking the old gardens of the Alcázar, to which there is a direct access in the east side. On the same east side is the entrance to the adjoining room, formerly known as the Sala Cantarera, now the library. Opposite is the doorway to the Chapel of the Gothic Palace.

The most thorough alterations carried out in this room were in the 16th century, when, during the reign of Philip II it was decorated with tiles and new Mannerist brackets to commemorate the celebration here of the wedding of his parents, Charles V and Isabel of Portugal.

The magnificent friezes of tiles are by Cristobal de Augusta who, from his workshop in Triana produced an infinity of ceramic pieces between 1577 and the early years of the following century: tiles, screens and friezes to decorate the four rooms of the Gothic Palace and gardens. These pieces feature the finest repertoire of Renaissance forms: gargoyles, caryatides and Atlantas, heraldic emblems, symbolic figures and portraits, all following a clear iconographic programme intended to show Charles as a classical hero. The emperor is portrayed twice, with his wife, in one of the tapestries.

Over the mouldings and borders of the grotto, in

which are depicted such themes as the fountain of life, is a frieze with the coats of arms of the different kingdoms ruled by the emperor (Castile and Leon, Navarre, Aragon, the two Sicilies, Granada, Toledo, Seville, Valencia). On either side are feminine figures symbolising the heroic virtues of Charles V: strength, justice, temperance, prudence. Also repeated between the pillars of Hercules is the imperial motto «Plus Ultra». The decorative tiles are separated by hermas including such classical figures as Proteus and Metra, as well as more allusions to the qualities of the emperor: thought and imagination, overcoming evil. Various pieces bear the signature of the ceramist AVGVSTA and the dates 1577 and 1578.

The stone brackets supporting the ribs and pointed arches were designed by Asencio de Maeda and built in 1577. Various painted canvases, imitating tapestries are presently displayed in this room, the work of Gustavo Bacarisas on the occasion of the 1929 Ibero-American Exhibition. The corridor leading to the gardens is covered by coffering by Hernando de Zárate in 1576-1577.

Tile in the Gothic Chapel.

Painting of the Virgen de los Reyes between Saint Hermenegild and Saint Ferdinand, by Domingo Martínez (1742). (Patrimonio Nacional).

Gothic Chapel. ▷

Gothic Chapel

Since its origins, the room situated in the western side of the Gothic Palace adjoining the Patio de las Doncellas in the Alcázar of Rey Don Pedro has been used as a chapel. It is identified in medieval documents as the Chapel of San Clemente, a dedication commemorating the day the city was conquered by Ferdinand. The architecture of the chapel repeats the arrangement of the previous room of the tiles, with Gothic vaults, Mannerist brackets and tiled frieze by Cristobal de Augusta.

The altar is by Diego de Castillejo (first half of the 18th century), and over it is a painting depicting the Virgin of the Antigua, an anonymous 17th-century copy of a medieval fresco in Seville Cathedral.On the walls hang various paintings on religious themes: on the west side, adjoining the altar, is a large painting of the **Virgin of Los Reyes between Saint Hermenegild and Saint Ferdinand,** by the Sevillian painter Domingo Martínez (1742), originally painted for the altarpiece in the chapel of the Palace of El Lomo del Grullo (near La Aldea del Rocío). Next is **The Coronation of the Virgin,** an anonymous 17th-century Italian work. At the foot of the chapel is **A Miracle,** attributed to Francisco Pacheco, father-in-law and *maestro* to Velazquez, dating back to the first half of the 17th century.

On the east side, we find, firstly, **The Story of the Adultress,** depicting the Bible story, but whose most interesting feature is the architectural setting, which follows the style of painters such as Juan de la Corte (last third of the 17th century). Finally, an anonymous painting in the style of Zurbarán entitled **Christ According to the Vision of the Holy Mariana de Escobar.**

Sala Cantarera (Library)

This room is symmetrical with the chapel, and is similarly arranged as regards vaults and tiles, varying only in the great windows which open up between flying buttresses from the old Almohade palace over the Garden of El Chorrón. The grilles are by Juan Barba (1583-1584).

The room takes its name from the fact that it served for many years for the storage of great earthenware urns (cántaros). In the 17th century it was used as the seat of the Sevillian Royal Academy of Letters (1748). The chamber now contains the library of the Reales Alcázares, which depends on the National Heritage Commission. The following paintings are displayed on its walls: «Immaculate Conception with Donor», attributed to Herrera the Elder (16th-century), «Apparition of Angels to Godofredo of Bouillon», by Federico de Madrazo (1839) and «The Imposition of the Great Red Cross on His Majesty Don Alphonse XII», by Ramón Padró (1876).

Flying buttresses of the Gothic Chapel.

UPPER FLOOR

Upper Royal Chambers

The Mudéjar Palace, following the traditional arrangement of the great Sevillian houses of the period, has an upper floor for use during winter. Of the original 15th-century structure there only remain two rooms, the Dormitory of Rey Don Pedro and the Audience Chamber. The other rooms are the result of reforms carried out under the Catholic Monarchs, with later adaptation and reorganisation according to the needs of official protocol. Since the 15th century, the upper floor has been organised to imitate the lower floor, with apartments for the king, the queen and the princes and princesses.

As these rooms are not open to the public, we shall describe only some of the most important rooms, for which illustrations are included here.

Oratory of the Catholic Monarchs

This is a small room for the private worship of the king and queen, featuring a harmonious architectural design and a fine altarpiece and altar in ceramic.

The Gothic-Mudéjar space of the oratory is divided into two by pointed arches, their interior decorated with perforated Gothic lattice work. That of the first was recently restored. The arches rest on brackets with mocarab base and a central column with bevelled capital. This, then, is a combination of Moorish spatial concepts with Gothic and Moslim decorative forms. The ribs of the barrel vaults are decorated with intertwining stems, leaves and small roses. The tiled altarpiece which forms the centrepiece of the oratory is a masterpiece of Renaissance ceramic art by the Italian Francisco Niculoso Pisano (1504), in which flat tiles were introduced to Spain for the first time. The theme and iconography allude directly to the Catholic Monarchs, the central section representing the Visitation of the Virgin Mary to her cousin Elizabeth, guardian angel of the Catholic Queen. Framing this scene is the tree of Jesse whilst the sides depict grotesque themes and in two victory crowns the mottoes of the Catholic Monarchs, the bundle of arrows alluding to their warlike power and the yoke with the rope and the motto «tanto monta» referring to pragmatism, one of their virtues.

The front of the altar features an Annunciation, with repetition of the heraldic emblems and initials of the Catholic Monarchs Ferdinand and Isabel.

Ceramic altar of the Oratory of the Catholic Monarchs. Francisco Niculoso Pisano (1504).

Details of the plastework and tiles in the King Don Pedro Bedroom.

Dormitory of Rey Don Pedro

This is one of the two 14th-century upper rooms surviving from the Palace of Rey Don Pedro. With a square groundplan and originally having two alcoves on either side, the main features of this room are the tiling, with starred lattice work, and the stucco work which completely covers the walls. The Mudéjar coffering is in three panels, its *almizate* or central section featuring two wheels of 12-sided lattice work, dating back to the first half of the 15th century. The room communicates with the Gothic Chapel, the Mirador of the Catholic Monarchs, the Gardens and the upper gallery of the Patio de las Doncellas.

Tradition has it that this was the private chamber of the Judge King, the scene of the story of the prevaricating judges, one of the legends attributed to that monarch. The story goes that in order to preserve the memory of the exemplary punishment meted out by the king to the four venal judges, he ordered their skulls placed in his bedroom. These skulls, as well as some of the Renaissance stucco work date, however, to the reforms carried out in the mid-16th century.

◁ *Oratory of the Catholic Monarchs.*

Dormitory of Don Pedro.

Audience Chamber.

Audience chamber

A rectangular room overlooking the main façade of the Palace. Its walls are articulated by stilted semicircular arches resting on columns with reused Caliphal capitals and black, white and pink shafts. The arches open on the side of the façade onto a narrow gallery covered by a lovely vault of mocarabs with a Granadan air.

This Audience Chamber contains the finest repertoire of Mudéjar decoration to be found on the upper floor, its walls completely covered originally-designed tiling and stucco work featuring the traditional motifs of ataurique, palmettes 16-spoked wheels, sebka panels and epigraphy. The coffering is in three panels with an octagonal central space, reconstructed in 1909 under the direction of José Gómez Otero.

These rooms, like the rest of the upper floor, are now used by the royal family for official functions in Seville, and one wing was recently adapted as a new Royal Chamber on the occasion of the 1992 Universal Exhibition. In the state rooms, most of the furniture and decoration dates back to the 19th century, to the time when the palace was prepared as the residence of the Queen Mother, Isabel II after her exile in 1878. There is a valuable collection of paintings feature particularly works by Romantic and locals artists, including Vicente López Portaña's portraits of Isabel II and Luisa Fernanda; Antonio María Esquivel's mag-

Ornate woodwork in the Audience Chamber.

nificent portrait of the Queen Mother with her sister; and Genaro Pérez Villaamil's «Investiture of Alvar Fáñez». The collection also includes works by Sevillian artists such as José Gutiérrez de la Vega, José Roldán, Manuel Cabral Bejarano and José Díaz Valera. Spanish painters from the Siglo de Oro represented here include Murillo, Luis Tristán, Francisco Pacheco and Arellano.

Finely-adorned vault in the Audience Chamber.

Detail of the Audience Chamber.

1
2
3
4
5
6
7
8
10
11
12
13
14
15
16
17
18
19
20
21
22
23
24

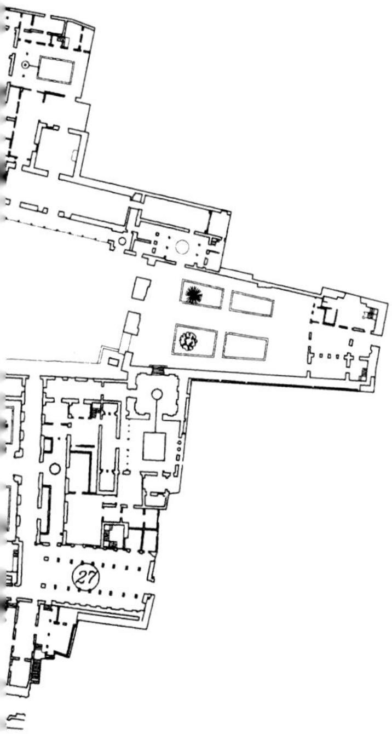

1. - ESTANQUE DE MERCURIO
2. - GALERIA DE GRUTESCOS Y MURALLA
3. - PUERTA DEL PRIVILEGIO
4. - JARDIN DE LA DANZA
5. - ENTRADA AL JARDIN SUBTERRANEO DEL PATIO DEL CRUCERO
6. - JARDIN DE LA TROYA
7. - JARDIN DE LA GALERA
8. - JARDIN DE LAS FLORES O DE LA GRUTA VIEJA
9. - JARDIN DEL PRINCIPE
10. - JARDIN DE LAS DAMAS
11. - FUENTE DE NEPTUNO
12. - FUENTE-ORGANO DE LA FAMA
13. - JARDIN DE LA ALCOBA
14. - PABELLON DE CARLOS V O CENADOR DE LA ALCOBA
15. - CENADOR DEL LEON
16. - JARDIN DEL LABERINTO VIEJO O DE LA CRUZ
17. - JARDIN INGLES
18. - LABERINTO
19. - TORRE ALMOHADE
20. - JARDIN DE LOS POETAS
21. - CAMINO REAL Y PUERTA DEL CAMPO
22. - JARDIN DEL RETIRO DEL MARQUES
23. - PUERTA DEL PALACIO DE LOS DUQUES DE ARCOS
24. - PATIO DEL CHORRON
25. - PABELLON DE LA CHINA
26. - PATIO DE LA ALCUBILLA
27. - APEADERO

ALES ALCAZARES DE SEVILLA

PLANTA DE JARDINES

JESUS MARQUINEZ RENGIFO

Pool of Mercury.

Gallery of the Grotto. ▷

THE GARDENS

The gardens of the Reales Alcázares form one of the most original and varied examples of this fragile art form in Spain. They unite styles and concepts ranging from secluded Moorish patios full of fountains and the light murmuring of water to the naturalist, tree-lined open spaces of English landscape gardening, passing through the imaginative architectural and sculptural elements and botanic geometry of Mannerist and baroque gardens. By chronology and location with respect to the palace, we can divide the gardens into two types - old and new - making up a total of over 15 different spaces, each with its own name and particular history.

The original nucleus of the gardens is found in the series of walled spaces adjoining the south side of the palace. Here are combined the taste for Islamic architecture and for nature. Delimited to the north by the fronts of the different palaces and to the east by the 18th-century Almohade *coracha,* which surrounded the old outer Alcázar, this area begins at the east end in the form of the Garden of the Pool, continuing with those of the Dance, the Troya, the Galley, the Flowers and, finally, that of the Prince, adjoining the western side of the Palace of Don Pedro.
The Moorish origins of this series of gardens are clearly manifested in their small size and closed nature, as well as in the materials used: whitewash, tiles to decorate handrails and fountains, and the

Sculpture of Mercury, by Diego de Pesquera (16th century).

Pool of Mercury and the Garden of Dance.

earthenware stones of the paths. The spirit of the Moorish garden is also maintained in the use of water, with spouts and irrigation canals, and in the vegetation, with orange and lemon trees and flowerbeds which, in the past, were combined with plots for vegetables and aromatic herbs.

Pool of Mercury

The pool which gives its name to the first of the gardens must once have been a great cistern, gathering the waters which from the Moorish aqueduct (caños de Carmona) flowed down to the Alcázares along the city wall, which now separates the new gardens from the so-called Callejón del Agua. Between 1573 and 1575, this tank was transformed into a Renaissance pool, encircled by an iron railing and decorated with bronze sculptures, overlaid in gold, by Diego de Pesquera and cast by Bartolomé Morel. In the centre is the figure of Mercury, holding his caduceus, his winged feet supported by a pedestal decorated with childish figures and grotesque gargoyles with water spouts. The little pillars supporting the iron railing around the pool are crowned by heraldic lions and *eolipilas* (ceramic spheres), each with a spout pouring water into the pond and dated 1576. The figure of the Roman god of trade was linked to the images painted in the niches of the grotto gallery, whose 16th-century originals, now lost, represented an allegory of the River Betis (Guadalquivir), given significance by the allusion to the prosperity of the Seville of the Siglo de Oro as the gateway to America.

Grotto gallery and wall
Puerta del Privilegio

This rustic gallery (1612-1621) is an exercise in Mannerist fantasy with which Vermondo Resta covered the old Almohade wall which surrounded the eastern side of the Alcázar gardens. The work imitates, with large doses of imagination, the models of the principal Renaissance essayists, particularly the books of Serlio and Vignola. The gallery combines elements intended to emulate natural geological formations through the use of sedimentary rock from the coast, with other, artificial elements, such as the stylised marble columns, whose capitals are mostly taken from other Moorish monuments, all based on the ordered principles of classicism.

In the first section, leading to the Pool of Mercury, the gallery is organised in two parts with blind arcades in the lower part separated by double pilasters crowned by brackets. The whole is colourfully decorated by the rustic elements of ashlar and voussoirs. In the upper section, there is a viewpoint (mirador) whose wide central arch is separated from the quadrangular vanos of the sides by pilasters, over which runs the cornice and triangular pediment. The mirador is presided over by a little turreted castle flanked by pyramid-shaped

Puerta del Privilegio.

spires topped by *eolipilas* (ceramic spheres). The arches and niches of the lower part were painted from 1618 to 1619 by Diego de Esquivel with representations of mythological themes. These Mannerist scenes were repainted and modified in the 18th century, and those we now observe are the result of unhappy restoration work carried out from 1897 to 1901 by the mediocre painter Rosendo Fernández.

The grotto gallery stretches beyond the pond, flanking the Garden of the Ladies and of El Cenador, where it broke off to delimit the area. In this second section, the lower part splits into two levels, one whose rustic ashlars form arches, mouldings and niches, and the other, above this, with arcades resting on columns forming a balustrade for the interior corridor. Over it are the high platforms which run the length of the walls. This second section features the Fountain-Organ of Fame, which falls over the Garden of the Ladies and constituted another common element in the complex and artificial world of the pre-baroque garden. Its hydraulic mechanism tunefully played the tubes of an organ as the water passed through. The fountain was adorned with sculptures representing Fame and the gods of classical mythology. The Puerta del Privilegio opens up in the Garden of El Cenador, communicating the old gardens of the Alcázar with the vegetable plots of El Retiro.

Garden of the Dance

From the Pond of Mercury, we approach the Garden of the Dance by a stairway rebuilt during the reforms of the 18th century. This area is made up of two spaces at different levels, and eight plots. The first spaces is presided over by two columns standing on high podiums where formerly stood the sculptures of Silenus and a maenade, both dancing, along with others of nymphs and satyrs sculpted into the myrtle bushes. The first platform of the second space has at its centre a little fountain with a fine 16th-century bronze spout, flanked by four benches covered in tiles by the brothers Jiménez (late-19th century), some of them imitating Renaissance models from the House of Pilate. The fountain has various water games, cleverly concealed spouts arcing water across the central platform. On the right of the fountain is the entrance to the subterranean garden described in the section on the Patio del Crucero or Garden of María de Padilla. At the opposite end, an segmental arch leads into the Garden of the Ladies. A small wicket gate in the western corner communicates with the Gothic Palace via a spiral staircase. The flora in this garden includes great magnolias which supply shade to the first space, the bindweed of the trellis which climbs the staircase, and acanthus, clivias, dates and other palms whose trunks are used by cats to sharpen their claws.

Concealed water spouts in the Garden of Dance.

Garden of the La Troya

Following the path which runs parallel to the south façade of the palace, the Garden of the Dance is followed by that of La Troya, whose rustic arcades are attributed to Vermondo Resta (c. 1606) and which was built before the Grotto Gallery. This garden features a number of busts, decorating the capitals of the pilasters and the bowl of the fountain, an ovolesque piece typical of 10th-century Moorish art, with spouts forming lions' heads. Over the columned gallery flanking this garden to the north are horseshoe arches with Mudéjar decoration, restored in 197-1977 by the then architect-curator Rafael Manzano, from the Mirador of the Catholic Monarchs.

Garden of the Galley

According to Rodrigo Caro, the Garden of the Galley takes its name from the fact that «there are galleys represented there, as if at battle: they shoot water cannons one at another...» By the 17th century, these playful elements had disappeared from the garden. Now, a column situated between its four plots commemorates King Al-Mutamid (1043-1095): «From the city of Seville to its king and poet Al-Mutamid Ibn Abbad on the 9th centenary of his lamented exile. 7 September 1091 - Rachab 384. Seville 1991» with, on the other side, the motto «There is no God but God» and the poem «God, decree in Seville my death and let our tombs there open in resurrection». This garden

Garden of the Prince.

Mannerist doorway to the Garden of the Ladies.

communicates directly with the Rooms of the Princes in the Mudéjar Palace through a broad terrace covered by a spectacular wistaria. Its verandah is supported by various 16th-century carved pillars. The flora contained here includes pacificos, dracenas and aralia papelera.

Garden of the Flowers or of the Old Grotto

From the Garden of the Galley, we pass into the Garden of the Flowers or of the Old Grotto, as it was known due to the false grotto which decorated it and which lost its rustic charm in the reforms of the 17th century, when it was hidden by the Mannerist door we now contemplate. The central niche contains a bust of Charles V. The cistern is covered by 16th and 17th century Sevillian tiles, and in its main front a tiny grotto contains a carved water spout. The small central fountain, in Moorish style, and the ceramic bench feature an interesting collection of tiles of te Delf type, embellished with the usual repertory of animal figures, female busts and landscapes. Among the species of flora which populate this shady garden are the specimens of palo borracho, a South American tree with a strange trunk, covered with prickles, and which flowers spectacularly in the autumn. There is also a large ficus and yellow-belled bushes.

Garden of the Prince

The first series of gardens surrounding the Palace is completed by the Garden of the Prince, situated on a higher level and accessible from the Mudéjar Palace. This is thought to have been originally a patio of honour preceding the Throne Room of Amutamid's Abaddite Alcázar. Nothing remains today of this pa-

Tympanum and fleche of the entrance to the Garden of El Chorrón.

tio, however, and the garden presents the aspect given to it by later Mannerist-style reforms and the large-scale remodelling of 1970-1976.

Between 1561 and 1626, the gardens of the Reales Alcázares were extensively reorganised in continuation of the work begun during the reign of the Emperor. The Royal Commission for Works and Woods, an institution promoted by Philip II, was the body commissioned with the conservation and extension of the Royal Heritage: palaces, gardens and hunting grounds. In the case of the Reales Alcázares, extension work affected particularly the gardens, which were increased in size to the tune of over 11,000 square metres through the appropriation of surrounding fields. A second belt of gardens was drawn up around the old gardened patios with the creation of the gardens of the Ladies, El Cenador de la Alcoba and that of the Labyrinth or of the Cross.

Garden of the Ladies

This Jardin de las Damas, also known as the Garden of Fame, has its origin in the 16th century, possibly having been designed on the occasion of the royal wedding. It was at the beginning of the 17th when the garden was reorganised in work attributed to Vermondo Resta and in which its size was doubled and it was adorned with gates and fountains in a predominantly Mannerist style. It is articulated by a longitudinal path, running from east to west, divided by three platforms, and lanes running around the edge, forming eight chamfered plots where plants, trees and flowers grow, delimited by myrtles. At the crossing of the two main paths was a fountain in Italian marble from Genoa, featuring a bronze sculpture of Neptune, a miniature replica of the sculpture by Giovanni da Bologna for the Piazza de Neptuna in

Garden of the Ladies and Pond of Mercury.

Garden of the Ladies: partial view. ▷

Bologna. The fountain was restored in 1897 and the deteriorated plinth, featuring dolphins, for the one we now see. The enclosure is adorned with gates and grotto fountains with designs after Vignola. In these, the formal language of Italian classical art is revitalised with new concepts highlighting plasticity and plays of lights, a tendency evident in the cushioning, frontons of mixed line, ovals and decoration of rustic ashlar, to which were formerly added the now lost terra cotta sculptures which alternated with figures carved into the bushes following the topiary art as described by Rodrigo Caro in 1634 and which represented the mythical scenes of Hercules fighting Antheus, the sea gods Proteus and Forcus, the judgement of Paris, and Diana surprised by Acteon bathing with the nymphs.

The gates communicate this garden to the north with that of the Dance and to the south with that of the Alcove. To the west, the Gate of Hercules leads to the Garden of the Labyrinth or of the Cross. The remaining side adjoins the Grotto Gallery, adorned here by the Fountain-organ of Fame, which we have already admired. The grounds of this area contain many concealed spouts which formerly transformed the entire path into a fountain.

The flora which embellishes the Garden of the Ladies includes high phoenix palms, an arboreal pitosporo, cicas, laurels, flowering peach trees, grapefruit, palos borrachos, pascueros, jasmine, syringa and orange trees. In the arcas of the fountain-grottoes grow tall cypress or paraguas.

Garden of the Alcove

After the Garden of the Ladies we come to that of the Alcove, originally an area occupied by vegetables gardens and incorporated into these gardens in the 16th century, when the pleasure pavilions were built. These are the Cenador de la Alcoba with, beside it, that of El León. Symmetrical to the latter formerly stood a bevelled pavilion, now lost. The flora which adorns this garden reminds one of old Moorish gardens, a halfway house between the market garden, the herb garden and the flower garden. Fruit trees predominate: orange, lemon, almond and date palms, alternating with such exotic trees as pacaons, azufaifos, paradise trees and love trees. Aromatic and medicinal plants and bushes include lavander, rosemary, thyme, sage, mint, aloe and laurel, as well as abundant flowers; roses, lilies, pacificos and jasmine.

Pavilion of Charles V

The Pavilion of Charles V, or Cenador de la Alcoba, presents a well-proportioned quadrangular volume, presiding over a little orange grove which has stood here since Moorish times. Originally, this pleasure pavilion must have been a funeral Qubba («Al-Qubba») presiding the Rawda, or royal cemetery of the Abaddite and Almohade dignatories. During the Islamic period, it was still used as a *musawa* or open-air oratory. During the times of the emperor, it was completed remodelled (1543-1546) into a perfect space for rest and contemplation. The whole work is richly decorated. The coffered ceiling is cupular with polygonal coffers, the imperial coat of arms features on all four fronts, and there are stucco friezes, Renaissance inside and Mudéjar out, as well as high tiled socles which adorn the walls. The layout is the original one and in it alternate ceramic pieces forming geometrical patterns and floral designs, including the name of the maestro mayor and date of the work - «Juan Hernández - 1546» - as well as a drawing in black and white tiles representing the layout of the first labyrinth which existed in these gardens. Juan Hernández was the son of the Moorish master builder Hamete de Cobexi, who worked in the Reales Alcázares in the early-16th century, testifying to the fact that works at the palace continued to be carried out by craftsmen of Moorish origin.

In the exterior, graceful semicircular arches resting on Italian marbles shade the central space, opposite them ceramic-covered benches and handrails. The tiles of this room, more than 5,000 in total, were produced by the ceramist of Triana, Juan Polido, in 1543, and feature a wide range of Renaissance themes and heraldic elements: the imperial coat of arms and the motto «Plus Ultra», grotesques: animals and mythical beings such as sphinxes, centaurs, unicorns, fauns, caryatides, tritons, etc, as well as floral scrolls: leaves and accanthus, vines and cardoon.

Cenador del León

This small Mannerist-style pavilion is attributed to maestro mayor Diego Martín de Orejuela (1644-1645). With a square groundplan and covered by a dome, the building features magnificent decoration in the form of mouldings and tiles, as well as decorative and heraldic paintings inside. Opposite the entrance and presiding over the great pond is a circular fountain with the figure of the lion which gives the pavilion its name, all dating back to the 16th century. In the north side is a grove of tall bamboo, close to a beautiful shady tree, whilst opposite is a fine palo borracho.

Garden of the Old Labyrinth, or of the Cross

The group of old gardens is completed by that of the Old Labyrinth, or of the Cross, reached through the Gate of Hercules in the Garden of the Ladies, or by a wicket connecting it with the Garden of the Flowers. This garden formerly contained the second labyrinth to be laid out in the Reales Alcázares. The first was probably in the Garden of the Prince or in that of La Troya, and whose layout is known thanks to the design imitating it in the grounds of the Cenador de la Alcoba (1546). This new garden echoed the Mannerist taste for mythology and artful play seen in the Garden of the Ladies. Its intricate bushes, shaped by topiary art, and the sculptures which decorated its central fountain were imbued with clearly allegorical mean-

New Gardens: labyrinth.

ing, alluding to the Labyrinth of Dedalus in Crete, the symbol of the triumph of Virtue over Fortune. It was built between 1626 and 1629 at the command of Philip IV, who commissioned the Alcaide of the Reales Alcázares, Gaspar de Guzmán, Count-Duke of Olivares, with its creation. The central space contains a pond surrounding the artificial Mount Parnassus which, in its day, was crowned by sculptures of Apollo, nymphs and Pegasus, with spectacular plays of water preluding baroque fountains. Now there only remain a few rough water spouts and a feminine sculpture in the grotto.
The botanical species here include tall cauarinas and palms, yuccas, bamboo, privet and pomegranate, all pruned to form bushes.
In 1910, Alphonse XIII ordered the removal of the labyrinth from the Garden of the Cross, and it was replaced some years later by that which can now be admired in a corner of the English Garden, opposite the Cenador de la Alcoba. This change was explained on moral grounds, as it was possible to see from the palace windows scenes of improper conduct which took place under the protection of the high, intricate bushes of the maze. Even during the post-war period, as Romero Murube humourously recalls, part of the daily duties of the gardeners included watching over the labyrinth and brusquely expelling from that Garden of Eden any courting couples who, in their opinion, were guilty of improper conduct.

NEW GARDENS

During the 20th century, the complete transformation of the old market gardens of La Alcoba and El Retiro into gardens increased the total area covered by the gardens of the Reales Alcázares by over 60,000 square metres. The new grounds contain three new gardens, the English Garden, that of El Retiro, or of the Marquis, and the Garden of the Poets.

English Garden

It was the desire of Queen Victoria Eugenia that the western area of the Huerta de la Alcoba should be converted into an English-style landscape garden. Contrary to the French and Italian traditions which proposed gardens delimited by neat lines and geometric patterns indicating the desire of taming nature, the concept of garden which emerged in the England of the 18th century romantically favoured the freedom and spontaneity of the vegetation, situating the botanical species in their natural context, without artificial embellishment. The idea is developed, therefore, of botanical garden, rather than the traditional private garden.

The irregular white paths circle small lawns in which bushes and trees are freely scattered, occasionally forming tiny groves. This garden contains some of the most unusual tree species to be found throughout the grounds of the Reales Alcázares, some of them very rare, if not unique, in this region. Firstly, there is gingo, from China and Japan, where it is considered a sacred tree by Buddhists, and one of the oldest species of trees known, as it has been present on earth since the Jurassic period. The tree population also features horse chestnut, oak, ash, cedar, yew, pecan, jacaranda, lagunaria, holm oak, araucaria and various species of palm and cypress. The modern wall surrounding this garden is covered by thick ivy and around it grow such ornamental plants as Adam's rib and elephant's ear.

Garden of the Poets and Garden of El Retiro, or of the Marquis

The old vegetable gardens of El Retiro occupied the corner formed by the Almohade wall of the Alcazaba, later transformed into the Grotto Gallery, and the defensive wall of the city. This great plot of land was gardened in two phases, the first between 1913 and 1917, when the twenty ploots to the north of the royal path were laid out by the then Alcaide of the Reales Alcázares, Benigno de la Vega-Inclán y Flaquer, Marques of Vega Inclán, during the reign of King Alphonse XIII, the second, involving the remaining southern plot, between 1956 and 1958, under Joaquín Romero Murube.

Following the route we propose for visiting the gardens, we enter the Garden of the Poets from the southern end of the English Garden, where we find the new labyrinth and an Almohade tower from the walls, now lost. This space is adorned by tall Himalayan cedars and a number of cicas. The present labyrinth was laid out in 1914 based on 16th-century models, its bushes formed by open-branched cypresses and cedars from the Real Sitio in Aranjuez.

The Garden of the Poets maintains the irregular, natural character of Romantic landscape gardening, for not in vain does its design owe much to the aesthetic theories of Jean Nicolas Claude Forestier, who landcaped the Maria Luis Park and the Gardens of the Marquis of Castilleja de Guzmán. These ideas were interpreted by the sensitivity of that universal Sevillian and poet, Romero Murube. From the French landscape gardener, he took the classical theme of the column as his focal point, whether the centre of arbours or exedras, and the great double pond in whose intermediate space is a baroque fountain brought from a convent in Sanlúcar de Barrameda. In its flowerbeds grows a beautiful rose garden, surrounded by bushes of eunonymus and cypress.

The Garden of El Retiro, or of El Marquis forms a rectangle two of whose sides are delimited by the walls we have already mentioned, a third by the royal

Garden of the Poets.

path which ran from the Puerta del Privilegio to the Puerta del Campo and the last by the wall of a building separated from the Huertas Reales (1911) and built between 1920 and 1921, during which time the old walls were demolished when the National Heritage Commission gave part of the vegetable gardens to the city for public use. This donation is now the Murillo Gardens.

The layout of these new gardens is attributed to the local architect José Gómez Millán, who was responsible for works in the palace and its gardens after the second decade of this century, first as assistant to his father, José Gómez Otero, and after 1920 as the official architect of the Reales Alcázares. The model for this garden is to be found in the palace grounds, for it takes as its example the regular arrangment of the Garden of the Ladies and that of the Alcove, with its rectangular plots and fountains at the meeting-point of its paths. However, the design introduces a number of novelties pertaining to the landscape gardening of the turn of the century, such as the use of pergolas and open arbours. Steps join the different levels, accentuating the classicist tendency of highlighting perspectives delimited by plants and trees. Sevillian tradition, too, is represented in the use of fountains, railings and benches with varied ceramic decoration, much of it from the kilns of the Mensaque y Montalban family in Triana. The carefully selected flora in this garden, alternating Mediterranean species with others from sub-tropical ecosystems, inof

cludes such trees as the following: cypresses, horse chestnut, pecan, ombu, jacaranda, magnolia, tall Washington palms; and fruit trees such as lemons, oranges, cherry, caquis, avocado, banana, pear, pomegranate, blackberry and a great vine which covers the arbour above the old Moorish waterwheel. The flowers include datura, coralitos, salvia rosa, jasmine, etc.
Before concluding our tour of the gardens, we should note the stretch of city wall which delimits the eastern corner of the Garden of El Retiro, or of the Marquis. This was recently restored (1993) by the present director of the Trust of the Reales Alcázares, José María Cabeza Méndez. This wall is a good example of the 12th-century Moorish defenses of Isbiliya, with barbican, moat and wall with sentry paths. In medieval times, it separated the palace from the nearby Jewish quarter, as well as serving as a support for the water channels prolonging the Carmona springs to bring water to the gardens and palaces.
We now leave the gardens through the Door of the Palace of the Duke of Arcos, popularly known as the Marchena Gate.

Door of the Palace of the Duke of Arcos

This impressive gateway to the Palace of the Duke of Arcos was acquired by Alphonse XIII at the auction of the goods of the house of the Duke of Osona, in exercise of the right of purchase at the same price to head off a bid from press magnate William Randolph Hearst, portrayed in the classic film «Citizen Kane», who had to be satisfied with reproducing the gate in his castle in San Simeón (Xanadu), California. It was installed in the Gardens of the Reales Alcázares in 1913 by the architect Vicente Traver y Tomás.
This is a magnificent example of the design of entrances to mansions during the time of the Catholic Monarchs. Its style corresponds to a fusion of late-Gothic elements with Mudéjar motifs and certain features of the new Renaissance repertory, a style called «Isabelline» by some historians in memory of the Catholic Queen.
Noble houses elevated or fortified due to their support for the unifying programme of Ferdinand and Isabel's reign of Castile and Aragon imitated the Catholic Monarchs in their artistic patronage, which began with the construction of urban palaces. The great lordly mansions began to emerge in the towns and cities of Spain during the late-15th century, the equivalent of the medieval castle, symbol of the militarised feudal society and of the limitless power of the nobility of that earlier period. These noble palaces had fronts with great doors opening onto a central patio, and represented the change of the courtly ideal and the lifestyle of the new age.
The Door of the Palace of the Duke of Arcos is, then, the rhetorical expression of the power of the promotors of its construction. The door employs the iconographic repertoire used by the monarch at the royal foundations, particularly the profusion of escutcheons symbolising the honour and grandeur of the lineage. The great dintelled door is framed by mouldings and decorative themes typical of the Gothic period: beading, foliage, small arches and lattice work of curves and countercurves. In the jambs and supported by two spired Gothic pillars are two sculptures of savages holding maces and shields, the work of Esteban Jaméte in 1544 to replace the 15th-century originals. The theme of savages and the heraldic motifs pertain to the new pre-Renaissance world of forms and models promoted by the first Spanish humanists. Both are tenant figures holding coats of arms, the left those of the Ponce de León family and the right those of the Cordoban Figueroa y Fernández family. Over the lintel of the door, a moulding decorated with traceria of lobes and foliage forms a conopial arch sheltering the figure of a lion, whilst above the arch, framed by a double frieze is a large window prolonging the height of the overall work. Between the arch and the first broken frieze are another two coats of arms, whose shape is typical of German heraldry, including in the upper third an armhole prepared to support the lance in jousting and tourneys. The left-hand shield represents the coat of arms of the Ponce de León family, dukes of Arcos, that on the right the arms of the Pachecos, marquises

◁ *Doorway from the Palace of the Duke of Arcos, Marchena.*

of Villena. The allusions to the Ponce de León family are completed by the installation of their heraldic animals, the lion and the eagle, on the spires. Some of the ashlars are decorated with cloves onn cardoor, forming a chequered pattern. The entire piece is flanked by two helicoidal pillars. It is thought that the door was made before the coming of age of the first duke of Arcos, Rodrigo Ponce de León, in around 1492-1496, when the continuity of the lineage was once more endangered by problems over the succession due to the lack of legitimate descendancy and the many bastard sons claiming the heirdom. The grandmother and tutor to the new duke was Beatriz Pacheco, a fact which explains the escutcheons in the upper section. The work is sometimes attributed to Juan Guas, who occasionally worked for the count of Arcos.

Passing through the door, we find on the left-hand side a staircase leading to the Grotto Gallery, which commands one of the best views over the entire gardens of the Reales Alcázares. The secluded area known as the Patio of El Chorrón leads to a covered passage to the Apeadero and the palace exit. The flora here includes oranges, bougainvillaea and a large wistaria which climbs up the outer wall of the Chinese Pavilion.

Patio de la Alcubilla.

Chinese Pavilion and Patio of la Alcubilla

This room is reached from the Patio of El Chorrón. It closes the adjacent Patio of La Alcubilla on the south side. The room was rebuilt in the early-18th century, during the reign of Philip V. It owes its name to the Oriental porcelain tableware kept here for use at banquets offered in the nearby Salas de Fiestas in the Gothic Palace.

The select literary history of the Reales Alcázares mentions the Chinese Pavilion as the venue of the meetings of the Mediodía group of poets, including the finest writers of the so-called Generation of 27, among them Federico Garía Lorca, who read here for the first time his «Lament on the Death of Ignacio Sánchez Mejias».

The Patio of La Alcubilla, also known as the «Tennis Patio» since one of the first tennis courts was installed here at the start of the century for King Alphonse XIII and Queen Victoria Eugenia. In the 16th and 17th centuries this formed part of the Alcaide's house, or Cuarto del Sol. Its present appearance owes much to the recent remodelling, during which the central fountain, made in 1600, was installed, having been brought here from the Sánchez Dalp Palace, as was the columned gallery leading to the Chinese Pavilion. Under the Mudéjar arcade of the north end is a curious version of the city coat of arms taken from the Convent of Santa Paula. Adjoining this gallery is a souvenir and book shop, reached from the Apeadero.

Apeadero.

Apeadero: 19th-century carriage. ▷

Apeadero

This was built in the early-17th century (1607-1609) and designed by the Italian architect Vermondo Resta. It serves as the main entrance from the Patio de Banderas and was situated near the old stables. Its wide door and spaciousness suited the new requirements of a royal palace, allowing the entry of the numerous carriages which would drive up to attend court receptions. Like a church, this element is structured around a nave and two aisles, separated by double columns of the Tuscan order, supporting semicircular arches. The side walls repeat this arrangement, with ornately-moulded pilasters and blind arches. The decoration and design of the room corresponds to the Italian Mannerist style Resta disseminated throughout the city. The impressive that we are inside a church is stronger since a baroque altarpiece representing the Presentation of the Virgin in the Temple, dating back to the last third of the 17th century, was installed opposite the doorway. This altarpiece is close in style to that which the Roldán family imposed in the polychrome Sevillian sculpture of the time.

Over this space is a high room used as the royal armoury during the reign of Philip V and now used for temporary exhibitions.

In the exterior, we can see the magnificent doorway of the Apeadero, a classicist work designed by Resta and reformed in the 18th century, as is narrated in the inscription in stone over the lintel of the central space: «In the reign of Philip the Third of Spain, this work was built in MDCVII, being repaired, extended and

Façade of the Apeadero.

employed as the Royal Armoury during the reign of Philip V in the year MDCCDDIX». The ceramic shield bearing the coat of arms of the first Bourbon monarch crowning the work was drawn by José Gestoso and replaced in 1889 a painting restored by Joaquín Domínguez Becquer.

The Patio de Banderas forms an essential part of the Reales Alcázares of Seville. It was the scene of many great parties and celebrations organised during royal visits, as well as others held on the occasion of the coronation of a new monarch or the birth of a prince or princess. In medieval times, it was the setting for tournaments, bullfights and jousting, celebrations which, over the years, took on more Renaissance forms. From the 16th century, the *fiestas* included spectacular ephemeral architectures and colgaduras, complemented by light shows, firework displays and the music of minstrels. All this transformed into a magnificent place of entertainment the urban space of this great square and theatre, whose spectacular backdrop is made up by the Giralda and Seville Cathedral.

BIBLIOGRAFIA

AMADOR DE LOS RIOS, José: *Sevilla Pintoresca o Descripción de sus más célebres monumentos artísticos*.–Sevilla: Francisco Alvarez y Cia., 1844.

AMADOR DE LOS RIOS, José: «Puertas del Salón de Embajadores del Alcázar de Sevilla».–En *Museo Español de Antiguedades*, Vol. III.–Madrid, 1874.

AMADOR DE LOS RIOS, Rodrigo: *Inscripciones árabes de Sevilla*.–Madrid: T. Fortanet, 1875.

BONELLS, José Elias: *Plantas y Jardines de Sevilla*.–Sevilla: Ayuntamiento, 1983.

BONET CORREA, Antonio: «El Renacimiento y el Barroco en los jardines musulmanes españoles». En *Cuadernos de la Alhambra* nº 4 (1968).–Granada, 1968.

BOSCH VILA, Jacinto: *La Sevilla Islámica: 712 - 1248*.–Sevilla: Universidad, 1984.

CABEZA MENDEZ, José María; García Tapial y León, José: «Recuperación de la Cerca Islámica de Sevilla». En *El último siglo de la Sevilla Islámica*: 1147-1248.–Sevilla: Universidad, 1995.

CABALLERO, Fernán (i.e. Cecilia Böhl de Faber): *Guía para visitar el Alcázar de Sevilla: breve reseña histórico-descriptiva de este célebre edificio en que se exponen sus tradiciones y los hechos más notables que en él han tenido lugar*.–Sevilla: Imprenta de la Revista Mercantil, 1858.

CARO, Rodrigo: *Antigüedades y Principado de la Ilustrissima Ciudad de Sevilla y Chorographia de su Convento Jurídico o Antigua Chancillería*.–Sevilla: Andrés Grande, 1634.

CARRIAZO, Juan de Mata: *Alcázar de Sevilla*.–Barcelona: Thomas, 1930.

CARRIAZO, Juan de Mata: *La boda del Emperador: notas para una historia del Amor en el Alcázar de Sevilla*.–Sevilla: Imprenta Provincial, 1959.

COLLANTES DE TERAN DELORME, Francisco: *Contribución al estudio de la topografía sevillana en la antigüedad y la Edad Media*.–Sevilla: Real Academia de Bellas Artes Santa Isabel de Hungría, 1977.

CHECA CREMADES, Fernando: «El arte islámico y la imagen de la naturaleza en la España del siglo XVI». En *Fragmentos* nº 1 (1984).–Madrid: Ministerio de Cultura, 1984.

COMES RAMOS, Rafael: *Arquitectura Alfonsí*.–Sevilla: Diputación Provincial, 1974.

COMES RAMOS, Rafael: «Imágenes Califales en los jardines del Alcázar de Sevilla». En *Laboratorio de Arte* nº 6 (1993).–Sevilla: Departamento de Historia del Arte, 1994.

COMES RAMOS, Rafael: «La puerta del Rey Don Pedro en el Patio del León del Alcázar de Sevilla». En *Laboratorio de Arte* nº 2 (1989).–Sevilla: Departamento de Historia del Arte, 1989.

CONTRERAS, Rafael: *Estudio descriptivo de los monumentos árabes de Granada, Sevilla y Córdoba: o sea la Alhambra, el Alcázar y la Gran Mezquita de Occidente*.–2ª ed.–Madrid: Imprenta y litografía de A. Rodero, 1878.

GAMIZ GORDO, Antonio... [et al.]: *Alhambra de Granada. Reales Alcázares de Sevilla: Dibujos*.–Sevilla: Colegio Oficial de Arquitectos de Andalucía Occidental, 1994.

GESTOSO Y PEREZ, José: *Guía del Alcázar de Sevilla: su historia y descrición*.–2ª ed.–Sevilla: Imprenta de La Andalucía Moderna, 1897.

GESTOSO Y PEREZ, José: *Sevilla Monumental y Artística*.–2º ed.–Sevilla: Monte de Piedad y Caja de Ahorros, 1984 (1ª ed. 1892).

GIL BERMEJO, Juana: «Los Reales Alcázares de Sevilla: notas históricas sobre su organización económica» En *Archivo Hispalense* nº 178 (1975).–Sevilla: Diputación Provincial, 1975.

GIL BERMEJO, Juana: «La Casa de la Contratación de Sevilla: algunos aspectos de su historia». En *Anuario de Estudios Americanos* nº 30 (1973).–Sevilla: Escuela de Estudios Hispano-Americanos, 1973.

GUERRERO LOVILLO, José: «La última Sevilla musulmana». En *Tres Estudios Sobre Sevilla*.–Sevilla: Real Academia de Bellas Artes Santa Isabel de Hungría, 1984.

GUERRERO LOVILLO, José: *Al-Qasr al-Mubarak: El Alcázar de la Bendición*.–Sevilla: Academia de Bellas Artes Santa Isabel de Hungría, 1974.

HALCON, Mª del Rosario: «El Palacio del Lomo del Grullo» En *Archivo Español de Arte* nº 257 (1992).–Madrid: Archivo español de Arte, 1992.

JIMENEZ MARTIN, Alfonso: «Dibujos de Arquitectura Sevillana 1. El cenador de la Alcoba.» En *Revista de Arte Sevillano* nº 2. (1983).–Sevilla, 1983.

JIMENEZ MARTIN, Alfonso: «Dibujos de Arquitectura Sevillana 2. El Jardín de las Damas.» En *Revista de Arte Sevillano* nº 2. (1983).–Sevilla, 1983.

JIMENEZ MARTIN, Alfonso: «Al-Andalus en época almohade». En *La Arquitectura del Islam Occidental*.–Granada: El legado Andalusí, 1995.

JUNQUERA DE VEGA, Paulina; HERRERO CARRETERO, Concha: *Catálogo de Tapices del Patrimonio Nacional*.–Madrid: Patrimonio Nacional, 1986.

LASSO DE LA VEGA, Alfonso: *The Alcázar of Sevilla: Guide to the ex Royal residense= L'Alcazar de Seville: Guide de l'ex residence Royale*.–Madrid: Marsiega, 1931.

LEON ALONSO, Aurora: *Iconografía y fiesta durante el Lustro Real: 1729-1733*.–Sevilla: Diputación Provincial, 1990.

LOBATO DOMINGUEZ, Javier; MARTIN ESTEBAN, Angel: «Dos Pinturas inéditas del Patrimonio Nacional en los Reales Alcázares de Sevilla». En *Reales Sitios* nº 122 (1994).–Madrid: Patrimonio Nacional, 1994.

MANZANO MARTOS, Rafael: «Reales Alcázares». En *Museos de Sevilla*.–Madrid: Patrimonio Nacional, 1977.

MANZANO MARTOS, Rafael: «Poetas y vida literaria en los Reales Alcázares de la ciudad de Sevilla» En *Tres Estudios Sobre Sevilla*.–Sevilla: Real Academia de Bellas Artes Santa Isabel de Hungría, 1984.

MANZANO MARTOS, Rafael: «Casas y palacios en la Sevilla almohade: Sus antecedentes hispánicos» En *Casas y Palacios de Al-Andalus*.–Granada: El legado Andalusí, 1995.

MARIN FIDALGO, Ana: *Vermondo Resta*.–Sevilla: Diputación Provincial, 1988.

MARIN FIDALGO, Ana: *El Alcázar de Sevilla bajo los Austrias*.–Sevilla: Guadalquivir, 1990.

MARIN FIDALGO, Ana: *Guía de los Reales Alcázares de Sevilla*.–Sevilla: Ayuntamiento, 1992.

MARIN FIDALGO, Ana: «Los Reales Alcázares de Sevilla: Digna morada de la Realeza Española». En *Reales Sitios* nº 111 (1992).–Madrid: Patrimonio Nacional, 1992.

MARTIN MINGUEZ, Bernardino: *El Alcázar de Sevilla*.–Madrid: Sucesores de Rivadeneyra, 1899.

MONTOTO, Santiago: *La Catedral y el Alcázar de Sevilla*.–Madrid: Plus Ultra, 1948.

MORAN TURINA, J. Miguel; CHECA CREMADES, Fernando: *Las Casas del Rey: Casas de Campo, Cazaderos y Jardines: Siglos XVI y XVII*.–Madrid: El Viso, 1986.

PAVON MALDONADO, Basilio: *Arte Toledano Islámico y Mudéjar*.–Madrid: Instituto Hispano Arabe de Cultura, 1973.

RAVE PRIETO, Juan Luis: *El Alcázar y la Muralla de Marchena*.–Marchena: Ayuntamiento, 1993.

ROMERO MURUBE, Joaquín: *Memorial Curioso de las obras llevadas a cabo en el Alcázar durante los años 1936-37*.–Sevilla, 1937.–Ejemplar manuscrito.

ROMERO MURUBE, Joaquín: *Discurso de la Mentira*.–Sevilla: Caja de Ahorros Provincial San Fernando, 1985.–1ª ed. 1943.

ROMERO MURUBE, Joaquín: «Los Jardines de Sevilla». En *Curso de Conferencias sobre Urbanismo y Estética en Sevilla*.–Sevilla: Real Academia de Bellas Artes Santa Isabel de Hungría, 1955.

ROMERO MURUBE, Joaquín: *El Alcázar de Sevilla: Guía turística*.–Madrid: Patrimonio Nacional, 1977.

TUBINO, F.M.: *Estudio sobre el Arte en España: la Arquitectura Hispano-Visigoda y Arabe Española, El Alcázar de Sevilla, Una Iglesia Mozárabe*.–Sevilla: C. Segovia de los Ríos, 1886.

VALOR PIECHOTA, Magdalena: *La arquitectura militar y palatina en la Sevilla musulmana*.–Sevilla: Diputación Provincial, 1991.

VIGIL ESCALERA, Manuel: *El jardín musulmán de la antigua Casa de Contratación de Sevilla*.–Sevilla: Consejería de Obras Públicas y Transportes, 1992.

INDEX

Protegemos el bosque; papel procedente de cultivos forestales controlados
Wir schützen den Wald. Papier aus kontrollierten Forsten.
We protect our forests. The paper used comes from controlled forestry plantations
Nous sauvegardons la forêt: papier provenant de cultures forestières controlées

3rd Edition
I.S.B.N. 84-378-1781-1
FISA - Escudo de Oro, S.A
Palaudarias, 26 - 08004 Barcelona
Dep. Legal B. 29929-1998